OP 1st 7⁵ᶜ

COMPUTERS AND
HOW THEY WORK

Computers and
How They Work

JAMES D. FAHNESTOCK

Ziff-Davis Publishing Company

NEW YORK

Library of Congress Catalog Card Number 59–15257

PREFACE

Depending on one's viewpoint, the electronic computer can be a highly complicated monster, designed and operated by supermen, or it can be viewed as a combination of relatively simple devices arranged in logical relationship to each other to do a certain job.

Unfortunately, the first viewpoint is the more prevalent one. Many people involuntarily suppress their curiosity about this new field with a feeling of hopelessness. This book has been written in an attempt to prove that, taken step by step, a computer is an understandable piece of machinery, far from a mystery. Computers are designed, built, and used by normal everyday men and women.

There are many promising approaches to the computer field today. Untrained and inexperienced people can learn to assemble and test the various electronic and electromechanical devices that go to make up today's computers. Numerous schools are available to those who show special interest or aptitudes. In these schools, some of which are offered free by manufacturers, special courses are taught that endow the resourceful graduate with skills that are in great demand in the industry.

Reference to any big city newspaper's classified ad section will vividly reveal the unprecedented demand that exists for experienced computer specialists. Those with a combination of experience and formal education in engineering or mathematics are most in demand.

In the writing of this book, a maximum effort was expended to achieve understandability without sacrificing technical accuracy. All the major areas of computer technology are covered, some in more detail than others, but hopefully in proportion to the average reader's interest.

Sometime during the reading of this book, the reader will find it instructive to visit a computer installation. Many large companies have installations that can be viewed by the public. Some of the larger computer manufacturers maintain operating computers in show rooms. Some of these offer conducted tours with guides specially trained to answer questions clearly and in whatever detail is necessary.

The technical material included in this book is intended as an introduction to the technician or noncomputer-trained engineer who is entering or interested in entering the computer field. The proving ground for this goal of understandability was the author's living room, where his devoted wife, Connie, agreed to act as guinea pig. Carefully avoiding the attitude, "if she can understand, anybody can," each paragraph was carefully rewritten until it met her standards for clarity.

In addition to expressing his appreciation for the invaluable service mentioned above, the author is indebted to the many manufacturers who so generously contributed technical information and illustrative material for the book. They exemplify the spirit of this young industry, showing their faith in its future and their willingness to assist in its promotion.

James D. Fahnestock

CONTENTS

8   Analog Computers   178

INTRODUCTION

Man's unending search for labor-saving devices has resulted in the discovery of many useful implements beginning with the lever and the wheel and extending to the harnessing of nuclear power and beyond.

Such inventions serve to ease man's physical labors and make possible the achievement of previously impossible tasks. They endow him with greater speed, which provides him with more time for the enjoyment of an improved standard of living.

As science has augmented man's physical abilities with mechanical developments, his mental processes have been enhanced by the advent of electronic computers. With electronic computers as a tool, many creative minds have been turned loose on unsolved problems, the solutions of which are greatly simplified and speeded by the use of electronic computation.

Thus, scientific development is a never-ending process. One invention leads to another, which in turn leads to another. The age of the electronic computer has begun, and it probably will never end. At one time the gas engine was an

1

oddity. Now most families own one or more automobiles, lawn mowers, power saws, or other labor-saving devices that employ gas engines. Some experts predict that electronic computation equipment will ultimately find uses not yet dreamed of by even the most imaginative forecasters.

Unfortunately, electronic computers have been glamorized to the extent that some confusion exists as to what they can and cannot do. They have been endowed with supernatural powers by overzealous advertising and promotion men who try to capture the attention of potential users.

Like anything new, especially something that is new *and* expensive, the infant computer industry has fought an uphill battle with those in industry who control the purse strings. But victory for the computer was inevitable and the computers' invasion of industry is an accomplished fact. Furthermore, the beachhead is constantly being widened and deepened.

It should be thoroughly understood that computers have and always will have limitations. They depend entirely upon human beings, directly or indirectly, for their apparent intelligence. However, under the control of a skillful operator or crew of operators, the electronic computer multiplies human creative ability almost without limit. Used to process routine data, computers lighten man's work load and take much of the drudgery out of his everyday life.

Today's large-scale computers help to make airplanes faster and safer. They help build automobiles. Guided missiles and space vehicles owe their very existence to electronic computers. Gigantic payrolls are prepared by machines. Computers forecast weather, design ships, control industrial processes, run machine tools, and solve tremendously complex business problems for private and government organizations. The list of tasks performed by computers grows longer day by day.

The computer was not always so versatile. It had its beginning many centuries ago in Egypt and China when an aid to counting called the *abacus* was invented. The abacus consisted of a series of wires strung on a wooden frame with several beads on each wire. Prior to its invention, merchants, hunters, and other number-conscious people relied on their fingers and toes or piles of stones to keep track of quantities.

In 1642, the French philosopher and mathematician Blaise Pascal devised a mechanical machine capable of adding and subtracting. Wilhelm Leibnitz, the German philosopher and mathematician, later succeeded in perfecting a crude machine with which he could mechanically multiply and divide. The generally accepted "father of the computer" was Charles Babbage, a mathematics professor at England's Oxford University. He devised and built what he called his *difference engine.*

Babbage's difference engine was comprised of a maze of gears so arranged as to assist him in solving some of his advanced mathematical calculations. He later developed an *analytical engine,* which superseded his difference engine. Both machines were outstanding examples of forward thinking during the early 1800's.

As the century progressed, increased awareness of the importance of keeping records led to the development of more-powerful computing devices. Herman Hollerith, an official of the U.S. Census Bureau, developed a computing machine that employed punched paper to store information so that it could be read and interpreted by machines. This was an important step toward automatic computation, as were the improvements and refinements made by another American, James Powers.

Mechanical calculators quickly earned the respect of those who understood them. The poorly paid clerk, whose job it had been to perform such calculations manually, was freed to put his mind to more-creative use—often to inventing new and better computing equipment.

During World War II, the pressure of military needs for ballistics data on newly developed weapons led to the conception and construction of the first electronic data processor or computer. American universities cooperated with various military agencies. Parallel projects at Harvard University and the University of Pennsylvania proved the practicality of digital computers when Drs. Aiken and Mauchly built the Harvard Mark I and ENIAC, respectively. The ENIAC was finished in 1945, the year the war ended.

Scientists recognized the potential of machines like ENIAC when it solved its first assigned problem in two weeks—a nuclear physics problem that would have required 100 man-years by conventional methods. Most of the 2 weeks was devoted to operational details and reviews of results.

The ENIAC computer represented a major advance in automatic computation. It was almost entirely electronic and many times faster than any previous machine.

Since ENIAC made its debut, many startling innovations have been introduced. Computers operate at seemingly impossible speed with virtually unlimited accuracy and with such a variety of configurations that they are finding enthusiastic acceptance in all branches of industry.

Strangely, although electronic computers are probably the most complex of all man's inventions, they are relatively simple to understand. They may contain many hundreds of thousands of parts but relatively few types of circuits.

Circuits are used as *building blocks.* Some computers use more of these building blocks than others. Some contain all available types; some have only the less-expensive building blocks, which keeps the over-all cost low. This book is intended to acquaint the nontechnical reader with the functions and operation of the basic computer building blocks and to show how they are used in combination to achieve the modern miracles of electronic computation.

· 1 ·

WHAT ELECTRONIC
COMPUTERS DO

"Just exactly what do electronic computers do?"
is a question that is often asked of men in the computer industry. Replies to this question can vary, depending on the
education of the individual asking the question, the degree of
his interest, and the time available to answer the question.

At one extreme the question can be answered by saying
that computers add, subtract, multiply, and divide numbers
at the command of a human operator. This answer is complete and correct, but it obviously lacks detail and would be
inadequate for even the most-casual questioner. At the other
extreme, the complete story of what computers do and how
they do it can best be obtained by enrolling in a full-time
course at an accredited school.

This book is intended as a compromise. The reader will
find all phases of electronic computation covered with sufficient detail for a working knowledge of computers, their abilities and their limitations. The reader will not become a computer designer, but he will be familiar with the problems

faced by the designer and he will be capable of appreciating new developments and techniques that are appearing every day in the field of electronic computers.

Going back to the original question, in a broad sense it can be answered by saying that computers can hear, remember, talk, and perform arithmetic operations. In an even broader sense, computers give the impression of thinking, but they cannot exercise the type of judgment that comes naturally to the mind of even the most inexperienced and, perhaps, poorly trained human being.

Fig. 1–1. A compact desk-model electronic computer manufactured by the Clary Corporation.

Fig. 1–2. A large room-sized system, illustrated by a mockup of the Univac Scientific 1105, built by Remington Rand for the Bureau of Census.

TYPICAL COMPUTER APPLICATIONS

Computers guide missiles and rockets, prepare pay checks, design new fuels, help to apprehend criminals, help to design highways, control atomic reactors, forecast weather, operate machine tools, and help to design and test airplanes and later guide them across the sky. In all these applications, the computer accepts information from some source, stores this information in specified compartments of its memory system, processes the information by means of sequential operations as dictated by the human programmer, and produces the requested results in the desired form. It works at fantastic speeds with virtually unlimited accuracy and with almost infallible reliability.

Computers have been credited with many undeserved capabilities. They can make complicated decisions that give the impression of thought, but their thinking is limited to the ability to weigh situations and to recommend a course of action based on ground rules set down by the human operator.

Fig. 1–3.   Typical of early electronic computers that have been turning out useful data since their construction in the early days of electronic computation is the EDVAC, which is installed at the Ballistics Research Laboratories at Aberdeen Proving Grounds, Maryland.

Thus man encounters problems in his work, and computers help to solve these problems. The man who originates the problem may never see the computer that solves it, although many other human beings may become involved in obtaining the solution to the problem.

Fig. 1–4. Large-scale digital computers are operated from control consoles whose multiple push buttons and indicator lights permit the operator to monitor the operation and to check the condition of various portions of the system. *(Courtesy Remington Rand Univac.)*

There is nothing mysterious about the way in which computers solve problems. Nor must the problems necessarily be tremendously complex to warrant solution by an electronic computer. Because of its tremendous speed and automatic sequencing, the electronic computer is capable of performing the required operations to solve the problems presented to it quickly and accurately, thereby saving its users both time and money.

COMPUTER CLASSIFICATIONS

There are two general types of computer applications. The terms *scientific* and *data processing* are usually used to define these two categories. There is considerable overlapping, and most machines are capable of being used for either type of work.

Scientific computation usually involves complex problems but relatively little information. In data processing, tremendous quantities of information are involved, but the computations are relatively simple. Most of the machines now in use are of the latter type, although they can be used for scientific computation as well.

One of the most common applications of electronic data processing is found in the maintenance of business records. A typical manufacturing company must keep voluminous records of money and material flow. The government requires certain types of records for tax purposes. Employee payrolls and customer-vendor billing procedures require myriads of records and computations. Add to these the basic requirements of banking, community relations, stockholder reports, sales and marketing analysis, production scheduling, inventory control, union records, and engineering, and the need for high-speed electronic data-processing systems will become obvious to anyone.

BUSINESS APPLICATIONS

One of the main virtues of the electronic computer is its ability to *store* information and to provide fast access to such stored information. The computer can store, for example, complete sales statistics, which are then available to the sales department for analysis purposes. Under the guidance of a skilled operator or programmer, the computer can interpret past sales figures and market figures and then predict sales, thus relieving sales personnel to do the work for which they are theoretically best suited, selling.

The production manager must plan his program and equipment to accommodate the sales department's predictions and known production commitments. He must assemble bills of materials for jobs. These must be scheduled, together with machines and operators to meet assigned completion dates. Because the computer can store and sort information, most of the above functions are greatly speeded and simplified and made more accurate through the use of electronic data processing. The computer quickly assembles bills of materials, calculates machine times for various operations, schedules operators, and relieves the production manager and his staff of routine matters.

Likewise, electronic data processing simplifies and speeds inventory control. As materials are received, notice is sent to the computer. Inventory records are updated almost instantaneously. Withdrawals are logged quickly and accurately. The computer operator can *ask* the computer for up-to-date records at any time. He can *instruct* the computer to keep track of certain items and to signal him the second that supplies run dangerously low, to permit replenishment before inventory is exhausted.

Payroll accounting is probably the most highly mechanized data-processing application in business today. Ostensibly, payrolls are intended to produce pay checks, but they must also accomplish many other tasks. Federal, state, and local taxes, labor-union dues, social security, savings bonds, credit unions, retirement plans, and many other details complicate the payroll picture to the point where electronic data processing is virtually indispensable if payrolls are to be up to date and on time. In addition, exact records are required for deductions for bonds, FICA tax, income tax, union dues, and various other deductions.

These are but a few of the many applications of electronic data processing in modern business. All such applications depend on the computer's ability to *take in* and *put out* information, to store appropriate information, and to perform the required mathematical manipulations quickly and accurately.

Fig. 1–5. Some computers are designed to solve only a few problems. The Stardac computer shown helps condition submarine-launched missiles for their computer-guided flights above the earth's atmosphere. (*Courtesy Epsco, Inc.*)

RESEARCH APPLICATIONS

Many research programs call for extensive electronic data processing. In the field of science, a primary use for electronic data processing lies in the processing of experimental data and the analysis of such data to extend man's knowledge and capabilities.

In the analysis of complex tests and experiments, parameters of interest (such as heat, strain, motion, pressure, etc.) are measured through the use of electrical yardsticks such as voltage and current. The resulting numbers are of little use to the engineer or scientist conducting the test since only voltage and current units are used. The designer is interested in degrees centigrade, pounds per square inch, feet per second, and other engineering units. The volts and amperes measured by the measuring devices must be converted to such useful forms. Such manipulations may be extremely simple, but often are extremely complex. In either case, where many measurements are involved, the electronic data processor is ideally suited.

COMPUTERS IN THE AIRCRAFT INDUSTRY

Typical of such applications are the missile and aircraft industries. In the early days of the aircraft industry, airplanes had relatively few moving parts, most of which were visible from the pilot's seat. Evaluation of airplane performance was usually conducted by the pilot. He watched his controls and evaluated their performance by feel. Very often the pilot was the designer and the builder, and he could make appropriate changes when (and if) he landed. Or he could explain his findings to the designers and they would in turn cut a little here or add something there until the pilot was satisfied.

As aircraft size and complexity increased, such hit-and-miss techniques became unacceptable. Instruments were developed that gave the pilot continuous indication of engine heat, air speed, rate of climb and descent, aircraft-altitude information, engine-operating conditions, and control-surface movements. The test pilot wore a knee pad upon which he jotted instrument readings that he could later interpret to the designers and engineers. In more sophisticated systems, cameras were rigged to photograph the instrument panel at regular intervals or at the pilot's command. Again data acquisition took a step ahead, and those charged with the responsibility of computation and analysis received more-meaningful information.

Other advances included development of compact, lightweight recording equipment and manual methods to convert the resulting recordings into computer language for high-speed data processing. Then came radio telemetry, and flight testing and electronic data processing moved another step closer together. Engineers and scientists recognized the inevitable marriage of these two fields. But there was a language barrier. The telemetry system produced wiggly lines on paper, but the computer wanted *numbers*.

Overnight, machines appeared on the market that enabled skilled operators to translate the wiggly lines into punch cards for computer entry. Again the human became the bottleneck, and results of tests that took several seconds to perform were not available for hours or sometimes days after the test was completed.

So the wiggly-lined paper gave way to magnetic recording tape. Tape recordings could be interpreted by high-speed machines. Another step toward automatic data processing was achieved.

Today, systems are in use that are entirely automatic from the output of the airborne-measuring devices to the final tabulated or plotted results from the computer.

Thus in the testing of completed aircraft, computers can help designers to anticipate troubles and to confirm their theoretical design calculations. They also play an important role in the processing of preflight structure and engine tests, and they aid in the computation involved in preliminary design work.

MISSILES AND SATELLITES

A great deal of public attention has recently turned toward the various applications of electronic computers in connection with guided-missile and earth-satellite research. Such vehicles can differ in many ways, for instance, in the type of navigation employed. Navigation is nothing more than determining and controlling the course of a moving vehicle by monitoring its position at various time intervals during its journey.

Position can be monitored by *looking at* the missile from the ground, or by looking at instruments carried in the vehicle. Another system looks at the ground from the vehicle. Ground observation is limited by the fact that distances traveled exceed the range of even the most up-to-date radar and optical tracking systems. Computers help to extend the range of ground observation systems by electronically connnecting a series of observation points so that one automatically picks up the vehicle as it passes out of range of the preceding point. Such computations involve extremely complicated calculations, and, because the vehicle will not wait, the calculations must be done almost instantaneously.

Using certain types of radar and other electronic techniques, a missile or aircraft can look at the ground, and a computer can be used to keep track of successive looks and to compute position during the vehicle's flight. These systems may be subject to errors or malfunctions due to external conditions, such as jamming and atmospheric conditions.

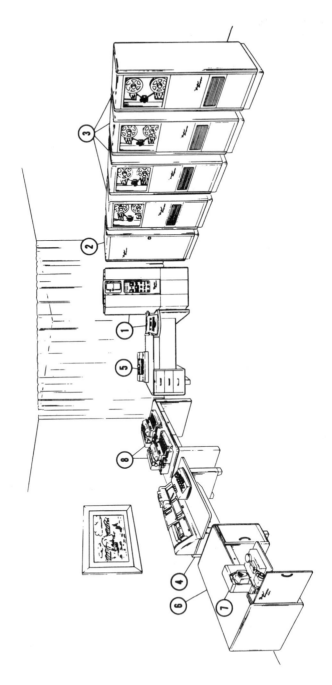

INERTIAL-GUIDANCE COMPUTERS

Owing to the limitations described above, the use of *inertial guidance* has become almost universal for long-range missiles. This system depends almost entirely on electronic computation within the vehicle for maintaining the flight on course.

In an inertial-guidance system, the vehicle carries sensing devices that are capable of detecting and accurately measuring changes in velocity. The computer's job in this instance is to process the resulting measurements in such a way as to refer them to the origin or destination of the vehicle, thus creating *relative* position information together with velocity and direction information.

With appropriate transducers (devices for converting one form of intelligence into another—in this case acceleration to electrical analogs or digital numbers), the computer can determine velocity, direction, and position. It can also use information thus produced to control its own course.

Inertial-guidance systems carry with them a reference object whose physical orientation is gyroscopically controlled to permit its use as a reference platform for acceleration transducers. By *telling* the guidance computer in advance what the desired course should be and by allowing the computer to constantly compare the desired course with that actually being computed from transducer information, virtually

Fig. 1–6. Even so-called "small" computers can become "large" in capability through the incorporation of extra peripheral equipment. The basic Bendix G–15 computer includes (1) a typewriter for input, output, and control, paper-tape punch, and photoelectric paper-tape reader. Accessories are: (2) digital differential analyzer, (3) magnetic-tape units, (4) punch-card coupler, (5) graph plotter, (6) alphanumeric accessory, (7) motorized paper-tape reader/punch, and (8) Flexowriter electric typewriter with paper-tape reader and punch.

instantaneous corrections can be made. The missile can be guided to its prescribed destination without external influence.

The use of computers in the guided-missile industry does not end with the guidance computer. Other computers must be used to compute position information with extreme accuracy to tell the guidance what its starting point is.

The foregoing examples of the ways in which computers are used in the missile and aircraft industries are typical of practical applications in all phases of industry. Computers are no longer practical only for large companies. Small and large companies now share the benefits of electronic computation, and it appears certain that its use will become even more widespread as the computer industry rises to meet the demands of users whose needs differ from application to application.

UNUSUAL COMPUTER APPLICATIONS

Computers have been put to many facetious tasks in an effort to attract attention to their amazing capabilities. They have been used to predict the outcome of horse races and elections, to play games, and even to play music (taking advantage of the fact that certain computer functions may cause audible tones to be generated). In all such cases, the computer follows the instructions of a human operator (perhaps via some prerecorded medium) but clever promotion men together with skillful programmers can make the computer appear to be acting on its own initiative.

Many extremely useful computer operations are similar in function to game playing. Computers are used to design computers. When furnished with a mathematical representation for each building block and problems to be solved by the new computer, a properly programmed system can quickly prescribe an optimum combination of the available building blocks to achieve the desired result. Some of the larger computer manufacturers have carried this technique to such an extreme that the men who do the wiring work directly from sets of instructions printed by the computer. Checking is done after the new computer is built because the computer has a better reputation for accuracy than the human checkers would have!

OTHER APPLICATIONS

In the atomic energy field, where extremely close tolerances must be maintained at fantastic speeds, computers are finding wide application. Reactor performance may be monitored continuously by a system built around a high-speed computer, with results in the form of control signals capable of maintaining the operation of the reactor at optimum efficiency and of anticipating troubles and initiating automatic corrective procedures where necessary.

Public utilities rely on computers for optimizing distribution systems. Civil engineers use computers extensively in designing bridges and roadways and computing highway cutting, earth settlement, and when making other important but previously time-consuming computations.

In the chemical and petroleum industries, spectrometer analysis is speeded by electronic computers. Huge refineries are "designed and tested" by electronic computers before the first piece of material is bought. Heat exchangers are designed, together with pipelines and other parts of automatic-process control systems, and, finally, computers are used to control processes while they are under way, to ensure uniformity and to improve quality, and to minimize waste during the processes.

Wherever possible, a computer is located at a point that is convenient to its users. Problems are routed to the computer location in many ways, but all must be funneled into

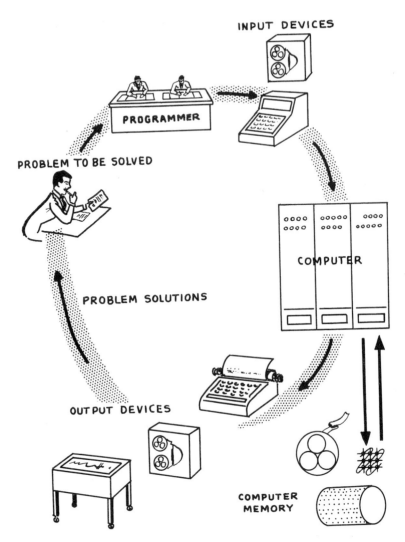

INPUT DEVICES

PROGRAMMER

PROBLEM TO BE SOLVED

PROBLEM SOLUTIONS

COMPUTER

OUTPUT DEVICES

COMPUTER MEMORY

Fig. 1–7. Flow of information in typical computer installation is shown in simplified block form. Originator of problem conveys problem to programmer, who prepares instructions and data in computer language using appropriate input equipment. Computer follows programmer's program, using appropriate storage equipment (drums, magnetic cores, tapes, etc.) and produces desired results on output equipment such as high-speed printer, tape equipment, or plotter. Results are returned to originator of problem.

20

the machine in sequence. Results emerge at the machine's output and must be distributed to the various users.

Figure 1–7 illustrates the flow of information through a typical computer installation, starting and ending with the man who initiates the problem. When the reader has completed this book he will be familiar with what goes on inside each of these blocks, and he will be able to answer the question, "Just what do electronic computers do?" In addition, he will know how they do it, and he will be in a position to discuss the relative merits of various types of computers and to appreciate the advantages of various types of peripheral equipment.

· 2 ·

COMPUTER LANGUAGE

The term *computer language* can have several meanings. To the computer man it usually means combinations of coded electrical or magnetic pulses or holes in paper tape or cards. In this sense it refers to a physical form of information that the computing machine can *read* and understand.

In another usage the term computer language applies to the somewhat unique language used in the computer trade. Although comprised of recognizable words and phrases, this peculiar language may be as foreign to the layman as the spoken word is to the machine.

INFORMATION VERSUS DATA

One of the more difficult language concepts commonly used in the computer field is that of *information*. This term is frequently used interchangeably with *data* to define the existence of intelligence. Intelligence can take many forms, and does in the computer field. One of the most common forms of intelligence is quantity. If we know how large a thing is, we have quantitative information about it.

Engineers, scientists, businessmen, housewives—in fact people in all walks of life make constant use of quantitative information. Through an elaborate system of standard units, people can define such quantities as weight, age, cost, volume, and height. Men use quantitative information in the form of numbers (together with units) to "keep track" of such quantities.

ANALOG VERSUS DIGITAL

Quantitative information can be presented or conveyed in two major ways. These two approaches lead to the major distinction between two widely different types of electronic computers, *analog* and *digital*.

The word digital refers to the use of a system of digits or definite quantities. Arabic numerals such as 1, 2, 3, and 4 are digits. The summation 2 plus 3 equals 5 is a digital computation. The number 2 means a pair of distinct objects or entities, and the number 3 we know from experience to be a digit representing a quantity that exceeds 2 by 1.

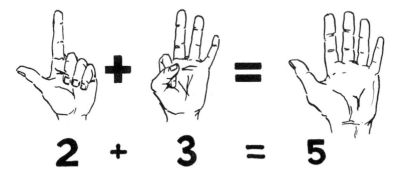

Fig. 2–1. Digital computation relies on the manipulation of numbers or digits that convey such information as quantity. In the above example, 2 plus 3 equals 5, we illustrate using fingers, but the numbers could apply to any other discrete objects. This form of digital addition is exact. There is no error.

When we say 2 plus 3 equals 5, the accuracy of the computation is *absolute*. There is no error. We can prove the relationship by substituting discrete objects for the numbers and testing the computation, as shown in Fig. 2–1.

DIGITAL INFORMATION

Digits are ideally suited to specifying quantities of discrete objects or entities, things that can be separated from each other easily with well-defined lines of demarcation. But not all quantities are comprised of integral numbers of discrete objects. It is simple to describe six automobiles digitally using the number 6, but it is somewhat more difficult to specify 3 gallons of gasoline with the same degree of accuracy. In such cases, we must know something about the accuracy with which each gallon is measured. Using the familar decimal-point system of specifying quantities that are not integral numbers of discrete objects, we can define quantities digitally to almost any desired degree of accuracy, provided we use enough digits and provide sufficiently accurate means for subdividing the basic measuring unit, such as the gallon measure.

ANALOG INFORMATION

When one speaks of a gallon of gasoline, or any liquid, he refers to a quantity of volume equal to that of a standard gallon as maintained by the National Bureau of Standards in Washington, D.C. In Canada, the term gallon has a different meaning. In Europe, the unit of liquid measure is the litre. So this type of quantity differs from the digital system. We seldom encounter 2½ automobiles, but it is also true that we seldom encounter exactly 3 gallons of gasoline, in the sense that the quantity is exactly equal to 3 Bureau of Standards gallons.

The type of quantity specification for which quantities are given with reference to a known standard is called *analog*. The quantity specified may include several types of analog references, such as gallons, quarts, pints, and ounces. If small-enough measuring increments are used, extreme accuracies are possible, but the quantity specification becomes digital because the number of increments involved is expressed digitally.

As might be expected, digital computers perform their computation using digits. When a volume of 3 gallons appears in a digital computation, it is handled as a number. The inaccuracies of each gallon measurement will be retained in all digital computations. An error of 0.001 gallon for each measure will be 1 gallon if the basic quantity is multipled by 1000 (see Fig. 2–2).

When a digital computer adds $14.75 to $2.34 the result is exactly $17.09. A digital summation of $1.00, $0.50, $0.25 and $0.01 is $1.76, with absolute accuracy (see Fig. 2–3). In some cases a result cannot be expressed with absolute accuracy. For example, if a digital computer is asked to divide 10 by 3, it will produce the result in decimal form to an accuracy limited only by the computer design. Even the simplest commercial digital machine can provide an answer like 3.3333333333 as a result. If desired, the computer can be made to "look at" the resulting number and to produce the closest practical number to the correct result. For example, if a worker earns $10 per hour and works $\frac{1}{3}$ hour, his pay will be figured as $3.33, since the penny is the basic monetary unit. This process is called *rounding off,* and all digital computers have provisions for accomplishing this rounding-off function.

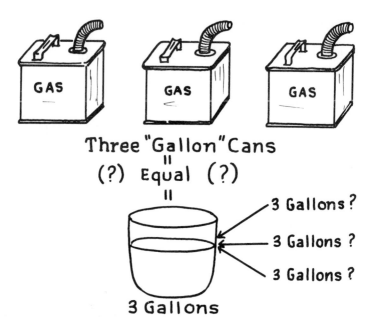

Three "Gallon" Cans
(?) Equal (?)

3 Gallons?

3 Gallons?

3 Gallons?

3 Gallons

Fig. 2–2. Analog computation is based on the manipulation of quantity-specifying analogs, such as the gallon when used to specify a quantity of liquid. The accuracy of an analog computation depends entirely on the accuracy with which each increment is measured. For example, 1 plus 1 plus 1 does not necessarily equal exactly 3 unless each increment is measured exactly—which is, of course, impossible.

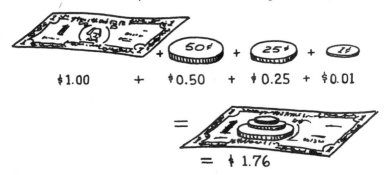

$1.00   + $0.50   + $0.25   + $0.01

= $1.76

Fig. 2–3. Money is always thought of digitally using the decimal-number system, with the penny (in the United States) as the basic monetary unit. Adding $1.00, $0.50, $0.25, and $0.01, the result is exactly $1.76. There is no error in such a computation.

A SIMPLE ANALOG COMPUTER

As an example of a simple analog computer, consider the automobile-fuel-gage system illustrated in Fig. 2–4. A float rests on the surface of the fuel in the tank. Through a mechanical and electrical linkage (or "computer"), a needle on the instrument panel is deflected *in proportion* to the quantity of fuel in the tank. When the level drops, the needle moves toward the empty mark. When the tank is filled, the needle moves to the end of the scale marked "full."

In this case, the position of the needle is *analogous* to the quantity of fuel in the tank. The needle position is an *analog* of fuel quantity, as the position of the temperature-gage needle is an analog of engine temperature and speedometer-needle position is an analog of the car's velocity.

ANALOG COMPUTATION WITH DIGITAL READOUT

In the latter case, it is usually important that the driver know his speed digitally because speed limits are posted dig-

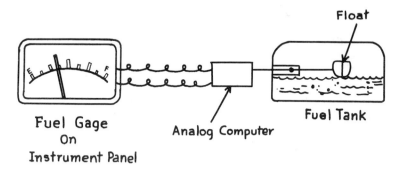

Float

Fuel Gage
On
Instrument Panel

Analog Computer

Fuel Tank

Fig. 2–4.   The linkage between an automobile's fuel gage and the float in its fuel tank is a form of analog computer. Quantity of fuel is expressed as a positional analog. Results need not be displayed accurately. The driver is only interested to know how soon he will have to replenish his supply of fuel.

itally. Unlike the gasoline-gaging problem, where relative information as to quantity serves the purpose, more-precise information is needed to define speed.

So the manufacturer provides a digital scale next to the analog indicator so that the driver can quickly and easily obtain digital information [using his eye to interpolate between marked points on the scale and the needle position (see Fig. 2–5)]. Actually, the speedometer needle can assume an infinite number of positions on its scale. The driver reads his speed in digits by visually determining the scale mark closest to the needle, or by estimating its distance between two scale marks where additional accuracy is required. The odometer (which tells the distance the vehicle has traveled) presents its information digitally.

It is significant to note that the analog device passes from one position smoothly and continuously. The driver "breaks up" the indicator readings of his speedometer using 1 mile per hour as the basic measuring increment. In doing so, he performs an *analog-to-digital conversion*. This task is

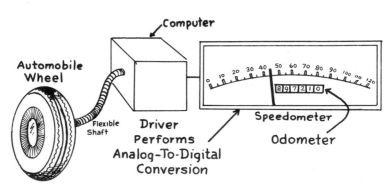

Fig. 2–5. The automobile's speedometer is also an analog-computing device, but it is provided with a means for visually converting the analog position of the pointer to speed in digital units of miles per hour. The odometer has a direct digital presentation for showing the number of miles traveled.

performed for him by the odometer. More will be said about the process of analog-to-digital conversion in Chapter 9.

THE SLIDE RULE, A FORM OF COMPUTER

Although pitifully limited in comparison with electronic computers, the basic slide rule is a powerful computing device. It is an analog device that is provided with digital scales for ease of adjustment and reading of results.

Briefly, the slide rule consists of two numbered scales arranged in such a manner that the product of x and y will appear a distance x (as measured with one scale) away from point y (on the adjacent scale). A few typical examples of slide-rule multiplication are shown in Fig. 2–6. Notice that the results in (a) and (b) appear to be exact. The quantity computed in (c) can be read with an accuracy limited primarily by the size of the slide rule. Larger rules provide more space between marks, and thus enable the user to interpolate with greater accuracy.

The slide rule has many of the attributes of the electronic computer. In a sense it has *memory*, since it "stores" information relating various numbers and their products. Broadly speaking, and assuming the presence of an experienced operator, it has the ability to accept and produce information.

Most slide rules have a number of scales. These provide quick access to other numeric relationships, such as logarithms, squares and cubes, and trigonometric functions. However, the slide rule needs external guidance for each operation if it is to produce useful results. Once the operator has "set" the rule, the results are instantaneous and continuous. But the operator must *read* the desired result—that is, he must isolate the desired result from a large number of simultaneously presented results. He must also mentally multiply and divide slide-rule scale numbers by appropriate powers of 10

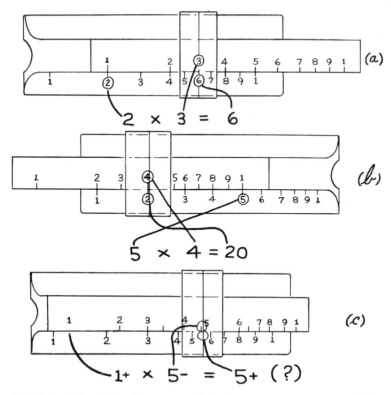

Fig. 2–6.   The slide rule is a powerful aid to computation, particularly for problems involving simple, limited-accuracy operations. Slide-rule accuracy is dependent on scale size. Operations must be sequenced by a human operator and results must be interpreted and written on paper for future use.

(10, 100, 1000, etc.) to make the numbers meaningful. He must also plan the sequence of the individual operations of a problem and must frequently write down partial results or commit them to memory for future use.

So we see that the slide rule is a useful and flexible device, but it is limited in speed and accuracy, and it must be operated a step at a time by human hands, be interpreted by human eyes, and be sequenced by the human brain. To be more useful, a computation aid should be automatic, fast, and capable of producing results to the desired degree of accuracy.

DESK CALCULATORS

The desk calculator is capable of much greater accuracy than the slide rule. It is a digital device. In adding numbers

Fig. 2–7. Desk calculators offer greater accuracy and higher speed than slide rules, but human sequencing of operations is required. Some desk calculators feature printing devices for recording steps and partial results. *(Courtesy Underwood Corporation.)*

it produces results of absolute accuracy. In the hands of a skilled operator, it can solve problems of considerable complexity with reasonably good speed. But it suffers the same limitation as the slide rule; it requires human sequencing of operations. It has no provisions for storing results; thus there must be an operator to read its results and write them down. Figure 2–7 shows a typical desk calculator.

The limitations enumerated above led to the development of electronic computers to eliminate the human bottleneck. Industry needed greater flexibility, higher speeds, and automatic operation.

ELECTRONIC-COMPUTER TERMINOLOGY

In the study of digital computers, frequent reference is made to such terms as *digit, character, bit, binary code, number, alphanumeric characters,* and many others. These are, for the most part, terms borrowed from everyday language. In computer usage they may be rigidly defined, and misinterpretation can result in considerable confusion.

A *bit* is the basic building block of any digital system. It represents an individual "piece" of information, for example, the presence or absence of an object at a particular location. The object is either there or it is not there. Think of a coin on a card, as illustrated in Fig. 2–8. In digital terminology, we limit the possible conditions to two: (1) the coin *is* on the card, or (2) the coin *is not* on the card. Only one condition can exist at a given time. This simple system has no meaning when the coin is half on and half off.

BITS, DIGITS, CHARACTERS, AND WORDS

In digital computers, bits are used in many ways, but always in combination to convey information about multiple-possibility situations.

Fig. 2–8. Digital computers operate by manipulating combinations of "bits" of information that can exist in only two definitely definable conditions. There can be no intermediate conditions. In the illustration shown, a penny on the card represents one condition; a penny not on the card represents the other condition. There can be no in-between.

In computer terminology, a *digit* is comprised of one or more bits. It can be a number, a letter of the alphabet, or even a space or a punctuation mark. The digit can have many possible forms, unlike the bit, which is limited to two. The word *character* and the word *digit* are often used synonymously, but a character is normally associated with four or more bits of information.

The number 7 is a digit, but the number 17 is defined as a two-digit number. Thus we see the possibility of problems arising because of word definitions. A *computer word* is a combination of bits or digits. The word 3456 contains four digits or characters. The word AX56L8 contains six digits or characters, and in this case they are called *alphanumeric* because both numbers and letters of the alphabet are used.

FLIP-FLOPS, THE BASIC COMPUTER ELEMENT

Computers process digital information by handling batches of basic bits. In digital computers, there are electronic circuits known as *flip-flops*, which have two stable states. To understand the flip-flop and its function in the digital computer, let us consider a mechanical analogy. Imagine a balanced seesaw of the type found in children's playgrounds (see Fig. 2–9). Let us remove the children and replace them with a trough with stops at both ends. In this trough, we will place a bowling ball that is free to roll from one end of the trough to the other end under the influence of natural gravity.

If an external force causes one end of the lever (previously balanced with the ball in the center) to be depressed, the bowling ball will roll toward the lower end. As the weight of the ball adds to the existing weight of the lower side, the external force that causes the original unbalance is reinforced by the force of gravity pulling on the ball. When the ball reaches the end of the trough, the system has assumed a stable condition. The external force can be removed immediately after the ball is set in motion, and the lever will continue to move until it reaches this stable condition. No further external force will be required in order to maintain the condition.

This condition of the seesaw can be assigned a *logical connotation*. For example, we could manually adjust the position of the seesaw (and the ball would cause that position to be retained) to distinguish night from day, hot from cold, yes from no, or black from white. The system can be used to *store* information. In computer terminology we say that the system has *memory*.

Pursuing the idea of storing night-or-day information, at dusk we might depress the near end of the seesaw. At dawn we would reverse the condition. Any remote device that is capable of determining the position of the seesaw can likewise differentiate night from day. Even a blind man (who could not *see* the difference between night and day) could essentially "tell time" by feeling the position of the lever,

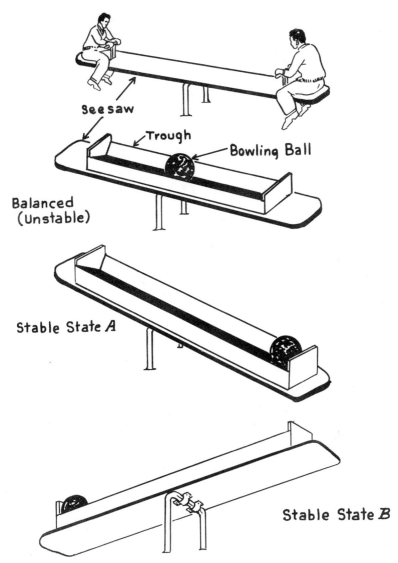

Seesaw

Trough — Bowling Ball

Balanced (Unstable)

Stable State A

Stable State B

Fig. 2–9. Digital computers are comprised of logic elements called flip-flops, which can be compared with the seesaws found in children's playgrounds. A bowling ball rolls to the low end under the influence of gravity and keeps the low end low until the system is disturbed. Like the flip-flop, one of two stable states must exist (except during transition between states, which is usually of short duration).

provided he knew the logical connotation assigned to the two possible conditions.

Notice that only two discrete conditions are stored. No attempt is made to store actual time of day. In one sense this two-state storage system is extremely limited, but if dawn and dusk are sharply defined, the system is capable of absolute accuracy.

INCREASING RESOLUTION BY ADDING BITS

Let us now picture two such levers placed side by side, as shown in Fig. 2–10. Because each lever can store two distinct conditions, the combination can store four different sets of conditions. These are identified in Fig. 2–10 as conditions 0, 1, 2, and 3, but they could be used to convey time of day with somewhat greater resolution, for example, specifying morning, afternoon, evening, and night.

Now let us imagine three such two-state storage devices. One might assume that such a system would be able to store 2 times 3, or 6, conditions, but we can actually represent 8 conditions with three bits. To illustrate, we shall "look at" one end of each seesaw and tell whether it is "up" or "down." This is all the information we need, because the other ends must be in the opposite extremes according to the rules of digital logic. Table 2–1 shows these eight conditions.

TABLE 2–1

No. 1	No. 2	No. 3	Condition
up	up	up	0
down	up	up	1
up	down	up	2
down	down	up	3
up	up	down	4
down	up	down	5
up	down	down	6
down	down	down	7

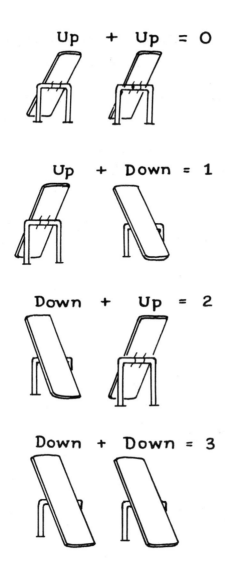

Fig. 2–10. Two two-state storage devices can define four conditions. Three are capable of defining six conditions, and four two-state devices can define sixteen conditions. This is the basis of the binary code.

Extending the above system to four seesaws, sixteen conditions can be defined. Any two-state phenomenon can be used to convey digital information. For example, lamps being turned on or off, switches being open or closed, or electron tubes and transistors conducting current or being cut off. To further simplify discussion of such two-state logic notations and to establish a common language that can be used in defining conditions regardless of the device, we shall adopt the use of 1 and 0 as convenient "names" for opposite and distinguishable states. Normally, unless the bistable device is perfectly symmetrical, the *zero* is associated with the less-active state of the device (such as the lamp being off or the switch being open) whereas the *one* refers to the more-active state. These states are thus sometimes referred to as the *on* and *off* states.

THE BINARY CODE

The reader may have noticed a relationship between the number of two-state devices or bits and the number of different conditions that can be specified. The relationship is an *exponential* one, that is, the number of bits used becomes the *power* of 2 to determine the number of definable conditions. Thus with two bits the number of conditions is 2^2 (2 multiplied by itself), or 4. With three bits we have 2^3, or $2 \times 2 \times 2 = 8$. With four bits we have 2^4, or $2 \times 2 \times 2 \times 2 = 16$, and so on (see Table 2–2).

This relationship is the basis of the *binary* code. It is interesting to note some features of the binary code. As a simple thought exercise, a person who uses his fingers to count to 10 in the usual fashion depresses the first finger of one hand to denote 1, raises the first and depresses the second to denote 2, and so on, until a count of 10 is denoted by the tenth finger

TABLE 2–2

No. of bits	No. of conditions
0	0
1	2
2	4
3	8
4	16
5	32
6	64
7	128
8	256
9	512
10	1024
11	2048
12	4096
13	8192
14	16,384
15	32,768
16	65,536
17	131,072
18	262,144
19	524,288
20	1,048,576

being depressed with all others raised (see Fig. 2–11). Each finger can be considered as a bit. We are defining ten numbers with ten bits. In so doing, we are extremely inefficient.

INFORMATION EFFICIENCY

Consider now the possibility that a person has been brought up on the binary system of numbers: As in the decimal system just described, he depresses the first finger of one hand to denote 1. Instead of allowing each finger to represent a single counting increment, he assigns ascending weights or values to each finger, as shown in Fig. 2–11. Doubling the

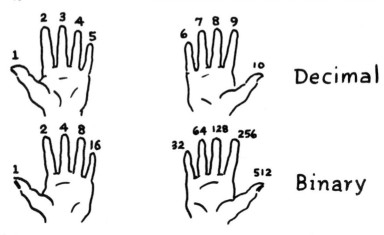

Fig. 2–11.   As an illustration of the information-conveying efficiency of the binary system of numbers as compared with the decimal system, the ten fingers of two hands can count only to 10 in decimal but to 1023 using the binary system.

initial unity value for each finger, the second finger is "worth" 2, and the second number in the count progression is denoted simply by depressing the second finger.

This still corresponds to the decimal approach, but after the number 2, the binary system reveals its merit. Continuing, without even using the third finger, the number 3 can be denoted. The weights assigned to fingers 1 and 2 add up to the number 3, so by depressing them *simultaneously* the number 3 is defined. The third finger is assigned a value of 4, so it alone denotes that number. Five is denoted by the combination of the 1 finger and the 4 finger, and so on.

With the decimal system we can count to 10 with as many fingers. With the binary system we can count to 1023! (Notice that this is 2^{10}, as predicted, if the quantity 0 is counted as one condition, bringing the total number of conditions defined to 1024.)

As numbers to be denoted increase in size, the binary

system becomes more and more efficient. In addition, the binary system and versions thereof are ideally suited to the internal workings of digital computers for other reasons, as will be described in Chapter 5.

COMBINATION CODES

The reader has undoubtedly spotted one flaw in the binary system. Few human beings *think* in terms of binary numbers. Even the highly trained computer specialist pays his bills and counts his money in the decimal system. The binary number 1111111111 is equivalent to 1023 but the binary number 11111111111 is 2047—significantly different, but difficult to recognize in binary form. How difficult it would be to interpret a binary number such as 1101001010, but its decimal equivalent, 842, is immediately recognizable to everyone.

There are many computer number codes that use modifications of the straight binary code. One of the most useful is the *binary-coded decimal code*, which is a combination of the binary system and the decimal system. Other codes include *octal, excess* 3, *gray, hexidecimal, cyclic binary,* and *biquinary*. Each has advantages and disadvantages. The computer manufacturer studies the intended application for his machine and selects the most-suitable code or codes. Some computers can accept information in several codes and can translate them into the code used in computation, then reconvert the results to another code for operating output equipment.

The binary-coded decimal code has many useful advantages in data-processing computers. All the arabic (decimal) numerals from 0 through 9 can be defined by four binary bits, as shown in Table 2–3.

In Table 2–3 we have used the conventional method of

TABLE 2–3

Binary	Decimal
0000	0
0001	1
0010	2
0011	3
0100	4
0101	5
0110	6
0111	7
1000	8
1001	9

symbolizing conditions through the use of 1's and 0's. In each binary number, the bit position on the extreme right tells whether or not the basic unitary increment (1) is included in the number. The second column from the right represents 2^1 (or just 2), the third 2^2, or 4, and the fourth represents 2^3, or 8. Thus the decimal number 7 is made up of $1 + 2 + 4 = 7$; the decimal number 9 is made up of $1 + 8 = 9$, or $2^0 + 2^3 = 9$.

The binary-coded decimal system does waste some possibilities. The binary numbers for 10, 11, 12, 13, 14, and 15 can also be represented by four bits, but they are not normally used in the binary-coded decimal system. To indicate numbers greater than 9, another group of four bits is used to represent each additional digit. For example, the number 34 is represented in binary-coded decimal as

$$\begin{array}{cc} 0011 & 0100 \\ 3 & 4 \end{array}$$

Usually it is more convenient to think of the binary-coded decimal bits as being arranged vertically, in which case the number 3586 is shown as

Thousands	*Hundreds*	*Tens*	*Units*	
0	0	1	0	8
0	1	0	1	4
1	0	0	1	2
1	1	0	0	1
‖	‖	‖	‖	
3	5	8	6	

Each decimal digit is thus represented by four binary bits in the binary-coded decimal system. Although this system is not as efficient as straight binary, it has the advantage that it can be interpreted at a glance. Conversion to straight decimal notation for activating input-output equipment that accepts only decimal information is relatively simple. The binary-coded decimal system is significantly more efficient than the decimal system, since each digit is specified by four bits as opposed to ten for the straight decimal system.

SIGNIFICANCE

In any binary or binary-coded number, the bits associated with the larger powers (the larger numbers) are referred to as being "more significant" than the bits associated with the lower-order powers. In a four-bit binary-coded number, the bit associated with 2^3 (or 8) is the *most significant bit* and the unitary bit is called the *least significant bit*.

CODE CONVERSIONS

Many computer "tricks" have been devised for converting between binary and decimal codes. The easiest way to visualize this is as follows. To convert binary to decimal we simply add the weights associated with 1 bits, as illustrated above. To convert from decimal to binary, subtraction is used.

For example, the number 21 is to be converted from decimal to straight binary form. The largest binary number (which is smaller than 21) is 16 or 2^4. Thus we know the binary number will contain five bits, the most significant being a 1, which shows that the number 16 is included in the number being converted. Performing the subtraction, $21 - 16 = 5$, we know that the next least significant number to 16 is 8 and that 8 exceeds the remainder. Thus 8 is not to be included in the binary number, and we use a 0 in the corresponding bit position. Next we test for the next least significant bit 4. We find that this is contained in the remainder 5, so we place a 1 in the corresponding bit position. The next number 2 exceeds 1, so we place a 0 in its position, leaving 1 for 1. The corresponding binary number is thus 10101.

The above operations are relatively simple to achieve electronically, but they are inefficient in terms of time. That is, they require more time and equipment than is necessary to perform the conversion. The more-efficient schemes are much more complicated. The above system serves to illustrate the relationship between the two systems.

Reviewing the two basic codes discussed thus far, we notice that the basic numbers involved are 2 for the binary system and 10 for the decimal system. We say that the binary system has a *base* of 2 and the decimal system has a base of 10. Notice that in counting (increasing the quantity in basic increments) the numbers to the right (numbers of lesser significance) periodically turn to 0. Each time they do, a 1 is *carried* to the next most significant digit position. In the decimal system a *carry* represents a quantity of 10, and in the binary system a carry represents 2. In either case, the position on the far right (least significant) counts units or 1's. Each count registered by the second position is equal to the base of the counting system, and so on.

OCTAL CODING

Because straight binary numbers are difficult to interpret "by eye," the octal system is often employed for purposes of visual display and comparison. In this case, the binary number is divided into groups of three bits each and the resulting decimal number is displayed. For example, the binary number 101001010 is divided as 101 001 010 and is displayed as the decimal number 512. Notice that decimal characters greater than seven will never appear in the octal system. The decimal numbers are meaningless as an absolute number, but for comparison purposes they are quite useful.

EXCESS-3 CODE

Another deviation from the straight binary system is the *excess*-3 code, which is actually a modification of the binary-coded decimal code. This popular code has several important and useful features. In some computer applications, it is necessary to subtract a given digit from 9. This can be done almost instantaneously if the digit is expressed in excess-3 code simply by reversing each bit, that is, changing all 1's to 0's and all 0's to 1's. This is called *complementing*.

Excess-3 coding is the same as binary-coded decimal coding, except that excess-3 codes appear to be 3 more than their binary-coded decimal equivalents, as shown in Table 2–4.

ALPHANUMERIC CODE

In computers intended for business applications, it is necessary to include alphanumeric characters as well as num-

TABLE 2-4

Decimal	Binary	Excess 3	Excess-3 complement
0	0000	0011	1100
1	0001	0100	1011
2	0010	0101	1010
3	0011	0110	1001
4	0100	0111	1000
5	0101	1000	0111
6	0110	1001	0110
7	0111	1010	0101
8	1000	1011	0100
9	1001	1100	0011

bers. These are not used in computation, but they are needed to identify numeric information upon which computations are being performed. For example, in payroll computation, the name and other alphabetic information must be stored along with the numeric information pertaining to each worker for activating the output equipment.

It has been demonstrated that four bits can be used to define ten numbers using the binary-coded decimal system, with five-bit combinations left over. With six bits per character, sixty-four symbols can be defined. Ten of these codes are used to define the decimal numbers from 0 through 9 in the normal binary-coded decimal fashion (using 0's for the two new bits). The remaining fifty-four possibilities are used to define letters of the alphabet and various other symbols, such as plus and minus signs, decimal points, punctuation marks, and mathematical symbols. Some combinations are assigned special meanings that can be interpreted by the machine as simple instructions, as will be seen later.

It will be important for the serious student of electronic computers to know and understand the different coding systems. Some of the reasons for favoring one code over another for a particular application will become evident in the discussion of computer arithmetic in Chapter 3.

· 3 ·

COMPUTER ARITHMETIC

In Chapter 2 it was shown that computers solve problems by storing data to be processed and "calling out" selected portions of this data for computation one step at a time. The actual computation is carried on in the computer's *arithmetic unit* (see Fig. 3–1).

COMPUTER ADDITION

The arithmetic unit of a computer is comprised of a series of electronic logic circuits whose fundamental operation is that of addition. To understand how most computations can be achieved by simple addition, let us examine a few typical computations. First, addition. To add the number 163 to 265, we arrange the numbers above each other and add vertically, using basic *number facts* learned in grammar school.

$$
\begin{array}{r}
163 \\
+\ 265 \\
\hline
428
\end{array}
$$

In step-by-step fashion, we say 3 plus 5 equals 8. We then

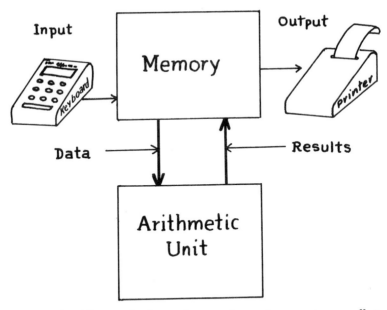

Fig. 3–1. The usual electronic-computer system carries on all its mathematical computations in a central arithmetic unit. The computer program arranges data to be processed in proper sequence to feed one set of numbers to the arithmetic unit with each operation command. Many electronic arithmetic units can add, subtract, multiply, and divide in as little as a fraction of a microsecond.

say 6 plus 6 equals 12, but we know that the 1 must be included in the next column so we "remember" the 1 and add it to the sum of 1 plus 2, obtaining 4.

SUBTRACTION BY ADDITION

Using certain "tricks" we can perform subtraction by means of addition. Manually, to subtract 163 from 265 we write the numbers as follows:

$$265$$
$$- 163$$
$$\overline{102}$$

Here we subtract one digit at a time, as before. In cases in which the digit being subtracted exceeds the digit from which it is being subtracted, we must "borrow" 10 from the adjacent digit.

Now let us see how the computer performs subtraction using addition. Electronically, using appropriate codes, it is a simple matter to subtract a number from the number that would result if all digits of the number were 9's. In other words, it is a simple matter to subtract 163 from 999 to obtain 836. This number is known as the 9's *complement* of the original number. By following a set of simple ground rules, we can use this complement to obtain the difference between the original number and the number from which it was to be subtracted. These rules may be stated as follows: (1) *add* the 9's complement, (2) increase the result by 1, and (3) ignore the 1 that appears in the left-hand position of the resulting sum. The result will be the desired difference. To subtract 163 from 265 we write:

$$265$$
$$+ \; 836 \text{ (the 9's complement of 163)}$$
$$\overline{1101}$$

Ignoring the 1 on the left and adding 1 to the result, we obtain the number 102, which is the correct answer. A few additional examples should be worked out by the reader to gain confidence in this technique.

MULTIPLICATION BY ADDITION

Multiplication can also be performed by addition. Consider the example in which 265 is to be multiplied by 163. Ordinarily we set up the following system:

$$265$$
$$163$$
$$\overline{795}$$
$$1590$$
$$265$$
$$\overline{43195}$$

Here, using basic number facts, we in effect say 3 times 265 is 795, 6 times 265 is 1590 (which we *shift* one place to the left) and 1 times 265 is 265 (which is again shifted one place to the left). We can eliminate the multiplication process as follows:

$$265$$
$$163$$
$$\overline{265}$$
$$265$$
$$265$$
$$265$$
$$265$$
$$265$$
$$265$$
$$265$$
$$265$$
$$265$$
$$\overline{43195}$$

In the computer a product of two numbers is obtained in this fashion. The number being multiplied is simply added to itself by a number of times equal to the 1's digit of the number by which it is being multiplied. The computer then *shifts* one position to the left and adds the same number as many times as the 10's digit specifies, and so on until the result is achieved.

COMPUTER DIVISION

Computer division can also be performed by addition. Let us assume that the number 33 is to be divided by 8. Using complement addition, we subtract 8 from 33 and examine the partial result to see if it is positive, zero, or negative. If positive, we place a 1 in the result register (a portion of the computer set aside for accumulating results) and subtract another 8 from the partial result. Since $33 - 8 = 25$ (a positive number) we insert a 1 in the result register and subtract 8 from 25, obtaining 17. This is again a positive number, so according to the rule we *add* another 1 to the result register $(1 + 1 = 2)$ and proceed to subtract 8 from 17, obtaining the positive number 9. Again we increase the number in the result register by 1 (increasing 2 to 3) and subtract 8 from 9, obtaining 1. As 1 is still a positive number, we increase the result from 3 to 4 and subtract 8 from 1. But now the partial result obtained by subtracting 8 from 1 is the negative number $- 7$. This indicates that the final result is somewhere between 4 and 5.

DIVISION ACCURACY

If we can be satisfied with an approximate answer, such a result could be adequate. However, digital computers are normally required to solve problems with much greater accuracy than this. To obtain greater accuracy, the number that remained in the partial-result register when a negative partial result was detected is increased by a factor of 10. We then continue the successive subtraction, adding results in this case to the digit position on the right of the decimal point in the final-result register, in other words, obtaining the desired result, $33/8 = 4.125$, which is absolutely accurate. Unless the computer is instructed to stop when the correct answer is obtained (zero remainder detected), it will continue until the capacity of its result register is reached. In such a case the answer would show up as $+ 4.125000000$ if the computer used eleven-digit plus-sign words.

It should be obvious that this method of performing division by subtraction (actually addition) would be extremely time-consuming if a large number were to be divided by a small number. For example, if 1000 were to be divided by 2, a total of 500 subtraction steps would be required before the partial result left the positive domain and the remainder became zero. To accelerate this process, a modern computer would automatically "try" (for example) subtracting 2000 from 1000 (obtaining the 2000 by shifting the 2 several places to the left in its register, or in effect multiplying the 2 by 1000). The result would be negative. The computer then automatically attempts subtracting 200 (after shifting 2000 one place to the right) from 1000, which it finds it can do five times before the partial result becomes other than a positive number. Five counts are added to the third-digit position of the final-result register. This process continues until the desired degree of accuracy is obtained. (In the example given, subsequent steps were unnecessary, since the result 500 was obtained with absolute accuracy in the sixth step, as indicated by the zero remainder obtained in subtracting 200 from 200.)

BINARY ARITHMETIC

In Chapter 2 the binary code and its advantages for information efficiency were discussed. The binary code is also uniquely suited to electronic computation. Most modern computers take advantage of this feature in one way or another.

To understand the merits of binary computation, it is important that a few basic number facts or ground rules be established. The number of rules necessary for binary arithmetic is far less than that required for decimal computation. Because all numbers are represented by 1's and 0's, only two states are possible for each digit position, instead of ten (0 through 9) as in the decimal system.

The following rules cover all possible situations in binary computation: (1) 1 plus 1 equals 0 plus a carry (the carry is similar to the 1 carried to the next digit position in decimal addition); (2) 1 plus 0 equals 1; (3) 0 plus 0 equals 0.

Let us examine a few typical operations. Assume it is desired to add 6 and 3, using binary numbers.

Decimal		Binary
6	=	0110
+3	=	+0011
9		1001

By way of review, it should be recalled that the 1's and 0's in a binary number tell whether or not the corresponding powers of 2 are included in the number. The binary number 0110 means

$$0 \times 2^3 \; + \; 1 \times 2^2 \; + \; 1 \times 2^1 \; + \; 0 \times 2^0$$

or

$$0 \times 8 \; + \; 1 \times 4 \; + \; 1 \times 2 \; + \; 0 \times 1$$

or

$$0 \; + \; 4 \; + \; 2 \; + \; 0$$

or

$$6$$

Following through the above addition, adding 6 and 3, proceeding from right to left in normal fashion, we find: 1 plus 0 equals 1; 1 plus 1 equals 0 with a carry, which we mentally place in the third column from the right; in the third column we now have 1 plus 0, which is 1, plus the carry 1, which in turn produces 0 with a carry for the fourth column; in the fourth column we have 0 plus 0, which is 0 plus a carry 1, producing a 1.

Regardless of the size of the number, these simple rules permit rapid addition of binary numbers. Using the previous numbers for comparison

Decimal		Binary
265		100001001
+163	=	+010100011
428		110101100

The binary version may seem more complicated, but it should be recognized that the binary sum is obtained using only three basic rules. The decimal approach required a great deal more previous knowledge of decimal digits and their relationships. It is much simpler electronically to implement binary addition than decimal addition. Binary addition is much faster when it is performed electronically. As a result, binary coding, or a modification of binary coding, is used in most modern computers.

SERIAL VERSUS PARALLEL ADDERS

It will be noticed that, in performing the above addition, we again attack the problem in a step-by-step fashion. Starting at the extreme right, we added 1 and 1 and obtained 0 with a carry, and so on. Some computers perform addition in this exact manner. These are called *serial* machines because they perform addition in serial fashion. Where speed is important, *parallel* adders are used. These are considerably more complex and, as a result, expensive. Let us first examine the workings of a serial arithmetic unit adder.

It will be assumed that the two binary numbers to be added have been stored in appropriate storage registers, as illustrated in Fig. 3–2. The right-hand (least significant) bit (pertaining to 2^0 or 1) of each number is transferred to a box known as an *adder*. This box contains electronic logic that causes it to produce at its output the results called for by the three basic ground rules of binary addition. The *sum* output is the 1 or 0 that results from binary addition. This bit is transferred to the least-significant-bit position of the result register. The *carry* 1 or 0 is transferred to a temporary storage position, where it is retained until after the initial sum is obtained by adding the two next most-significant bits. The result of this sum plus the carry are treated in a manner similar to the first, and so on until all bits of both numbers have been processed and the final sum appears in the output register.

The electronic components employed in adders vary from computer to computer. Some use magnetic elements, others use tubes, transistors, or diodes. Taking everything into consideration, a full-fledged adder has three inputs and

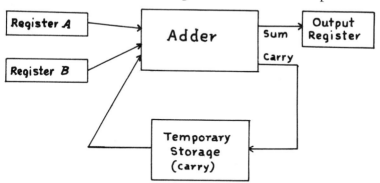

Fig. 3–2. In a serial type of electronic computer, numbers to be added are temporarily stored in registers that can be read out serially (one bit at a time) in such a way that a single adder circuit accommodates all addition requirements. The temporary storage registers can be in the form of a drum track of registers comprised of such elements as transistor flip-flops or magnetic elements.

two outputs. Two of the inputs are for data, the third being reserved for possible carries from previous (less-significant) bits. The outputs are sum and carry.

ELECTRONIC ADDERS

To understand the workings of an adder, a few basic digital techniques must be discussed. Consider the simple sketch shown in Fig. 3–3. Two roads are shown and each road contains two drawbridges. Let us assign digital logic names to the two possible positions of the drawbridges; a closed bridge will be represented by a 1 and an open bridge will be represented by a 0 (a closed bridge permitting passage along the road, an open bridge obstructing passage). In this case, the bridge positions constitute the *digital input* to the logic system.

In Fig. 3–3a, *both* bridges must be closed for passage from *start* to *finish*. In Fig. 3–3b, *either* bridge must be closed for passage.

The electronic equivalents of these simple examples are AND and OR gates, respectively. They are symbolized in Fig. 3–4. In computer terminology their functions are as follows: In the case of the AND gate, a 1 will appear at the output *only* if 1's are applied to *both* inputs; otherwise the output will be 0. In the case of the OR gate, a 1 will appear at the output if a 1 is applied to *either* input terminal; only if 0's are applied to both inputs will the output of the OR gate be 0.

THE HALF ADDER

Let us see how these simple logic elements can be combined to fulfill the requirements of the binary-addition ground rules. It is convenient to approach this problem in two steps.

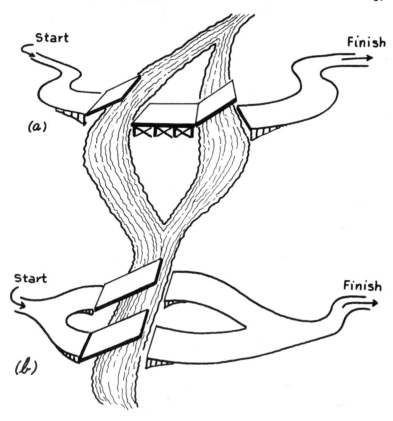

Start

Finish

(a)

Start

Finish

(b)

Fig. 3–3. Most computer operations depend on the ability of logic circuits to perform the AND and OR functions. In (a) the path from start to finish will be complete if and only if *both* bridges are closed— thus the name AND gate. In (b) *either* bridge being closed will cause completion of the path—thus the name OR gate.

First we will discuss a circuit that is capable of performing half of the logic required for binary addition—thus the name *half adder*. Figure 3–5 shows a half adder in electronic symbology.

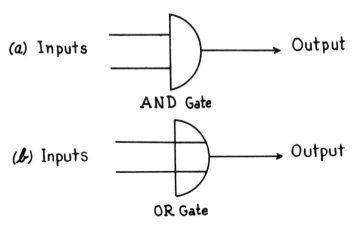

(a) Inputs

Output

AND Gate

(b) Inputs

Output

OR Gate

Fig. 3–4.   Symbols for AND and OR gates are frequently used in computer writings and schematic diagrams. In (a) 1's must be applied to both inputs to obtain a 1 output. In (b) a 1 can be applied to *either or both* inputs to obtain an output. The arrowheads can be eliminated from the AND-gate inputs.

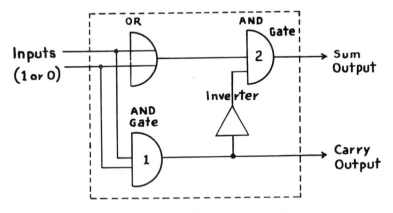

Inputs
(1 or 0)

OR

AND Gate
2

Sum
Output

Inverter

AND
Gate

1

Carry
Output

Fig. 3–5.   The half adder, basic element of any electronic-computer arithmetic unit, is comprised of two AND gates, one OR gate, and a logic inverter. The half adder has no provisions for accepting a carry input from a previous stage or from a previous summation.

Reviewing, the function of the OR gate is to produce a logical 1 whenever a 1 is applied to either or both of its inputs and a 0 when both inputs are 0. The AND gate produces a 1 at its output only when *both* inputs are 1's. The *inverter* simply inverts (changes from 1 to 0 or from 0 to 1) the logic of a signal applied to its input.

Referring to Fig. 3–5, if the two 1's are applied to the adder inputs, the OR gate will produce a 1 that will be applied to one of the inputs of AND gate 2. The two input 1's will also be applied to the input of AND gate 1, and, because both of its inputs are 1's in this case, it will produce a 1 at its output. The output of AND gate 1 is the *carry* output, thus we have produced the required carry. But inputs of binary 1 plus binary 1 should yield no sum output, and this condition is likewise fulfilled. The 1 output of AND gate 1 is changed to a 0 by the inverter and is applied to the second input of AND gate 2. Because this input is a 0 and because both inputs must be 1's for an AND gate to produce a 1 output, the output of AND gate 2 is 0, as required.

Now let us consider the case with a 1 and a 0 applied to the adder input terminals. The OR gate produces a 1 output because one of its inputs is a 1. This 1 is applied to one of the inputs of AND gate 2. The inputs to AND gate 1 are not both 1's in this case. Thus no carry output is produced, as required. However, the 0 output of AND gate 1 is inverted to a.1 by the inverter and applied to the second input of AND gate 2, where, combined with the 1 input from the OR gate, it causes a 1 to be produced at the output of AND gate 2 and the sum output, again fulfilling the requirements of binary addition.

The final ground rule, binary 0 plus binary 0 equals binary 0, is likewise accommodated. Two 0's applied to the OR gate produce a 0 at its output, which automatically causes the sum output to be 0 (because at least one of the inputs to AND gate 2 is a 0). The AND gate 1 fails to produce a 1, as both of its inputs are 0's, thus preventing a carry output. Although the inverter applies a 1 to the second input of AND gate 2, the sum output is 0 because of the 0 applied from the OR gate.

FULL ADDERS

Half adders can be used in combination, together with an additional component or two, to perform the complete process of binary addition. It should be noticed that the half adder has only two inputs, and a full adder requires three (one for the carry from the next least-significant bit). It will be instructive for the reader to substitute the basic components for the blocks shown in Fig. 3–6 to fully appreciate the logical function of the full adder.

With appropriate storage and timing provisions, a single half adder can be used to perform most of the computations required of an electronic computer. Such an arrangement would result in a rather slow and probably inflexible machine. Therefore, computer manufacturers have made numerous refinements to the basic half adder and have used these re-

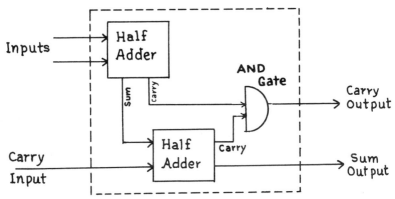

Fig. 3–6.   The binary adder has three inputs and two outputs to fulfill all the requirements for binary addition. It is comprised of two half adders and an AND gate. With proper timing circuits, a single adder can accommodate a wide variety of arithmetic operations.

finements in combinations to achieve the desired results with minimum time wasted. In some computers, numbers containing thirty-six bits or more can be added in less than a millionth of a second! Reduction of the basic addition time inevitably speeds other operations, as all are related to or dependent on addition.

One thing should be understood. The computer user is seldom concerned with the electronic procedure that is used to perform arithmetic operations. The programmer simply specifies two numbers to be processed, causes them to be transferred to a position within the computer at which they can be processed, and initiates a routine in which all the steps required for the operation are performed automatically and efficiently.

· 4 ·

DIGITAL-COMPUTER
PROGRAMMING

A man standing in the heart of New York City and wanting to travel to Washington, D.C., is faced with a problem that requires a solution (see Fig. 4–1). Shall he walk, run, drive his car, or take a bus, train, airplane, or guided missile?

Walking would be a poor choice for obvious reasons. It might be possible to transport man in a guided missile, but this choice is likewise ridiculous.

SELECTING THE ROUTE

Once the mode of transportation has been selected, other factors must be considered along the pathway to the solution of his problem. Let us assume that he chooses to drive his automobile. What route shall he take? Which tunnel or bridge to reach New Jersey? Shall he use the speedy New Jersey Turnpike or the practically parallel free highway? Are there any short cuts? Should he pay a few cents to use the Baltimore Harbor Tunnel, and thereby save considerable

Fig. 4–1. When faced with a problem, man must first select the appropriate aid to assist him in arriving at a solution. In travel he must first select his mode of transportation.

time, or should he drive through the city of Baltimore and save the money? When he reaches the outskirts of Washington (strictly speaking his problem is solved) he must consider the best way to get to his specific destination in the city. He must park his car and he should arrive dressed in a manner that is suitable for the occasion.

Reviewing the man's situation, he has a problem, and in arriving at a solution he finds himself faced with a number of smaller subproblems. The man who has the experience to make each decision correctly will get more out of his limited capabilities than the inexperienced man. He can reach Washington in many different ways, some more scenic, some more costly, some faster, and some more comfortable than others.

SELECTING A COMPUTATION AID

In the solution of mathematical problems the situation is quite similar. Man finds himself equipped with numerous aids for arriving at solutions, for example, pencil and paper, slide rules, desk calculators, and small, medium, and large computers (see Fig. 4–2). His first choice, like selecting his mode of transportation, is to choose his aid.

This choice will be guided by availability and practicality. No aid is required to add 2 and 2. A pencil and paper will serve nicely for the simple calculations that are encountered

Fig. 4–2. In computation man must make a selection from such available aids as the slide rule, the desk calculator, or the electronic computer. Because the latter is automatic, it must be programmed properly for maximum speed and efficiency.

only occasionally and in limited quantities. Slide rules and calculators are faster and more flexible, and electronic computers offer their assistance in solving problems that involve large quantities of data at high speeds and with almost unlimited accuracies.

PROGRAMMING THE COMPUTER

Having selected his aid, the "route" problem arises. As an example, consider the problem of solving the algebraic equation $y = ab + ac$ for the value of y if a, b, and c are given. This problem can be solved by multiplying a times b, then multiplying a times c, and then adding the two products to reach the desired solution. A trained mathematician will quickly recognize the equivalence of the formula $y = a(b + c)$. With this route or approach, he can reach the same solution in *two* steps instead of three. He simply adds b and c and multiplies the result by a.

Even in this simple example several less-obvious factors must be considered in selecting a route. Surprisingly enough, under certain circumstances, the actual results may differ between the two approaches suggested above. (The reason for such differences is somewhat complicated and involves the rounding-off feature of computers. This will be discussed later.)

Making these types of decisions, or the route selection, is the job of the *computer programmer*. It should be understood that with very little training even a small child could be taught to "program" a large computer, just as a child could be trained to decide whether to travel to Washington by way of Alaska or Baltimore. However, most computer problems differ in one or more respects, and efficient use of computation and data-processing equipment is directly dependent on the programmer's experience and ingenuity.

COMPUTER-CENTER OPERATION

In most computer centers, work for a computer can come from a number of sources. Normally, the originator of the work contacts a scheduler, who considers the relative urgency of the work from all sources and prepares an appropriate schedule. As a rule, the scheduler has a supply of low-priority work that he can fall back on when special work is in short supply.

Problems can arrive in various ways. Some may be scratched on pieces of paper with only a few basic numbers to be manipulated. Other work may come from an engineer's notebook that contains accumulated data from tests and has mathematical equations to solve based on the data. Other work may take the form of punch cards, perforated tape, or magnetic tape containing thousands or millions of digitally recorded numbers, all of which must be processed according to formulas of varying complexity.

Again considering a typical installation, the programmer is given the responsibility to select the route the computer will take in solving each particular problem. He maps out a detailed route, including all known short cuts. To do an efficient job of routing, he must know his machine in exact detail. He must know its weak points and avoid them. He must also know its strong points and be able to take advantage of them.

The programmer's map must be put into language that the machine can understand. Computers have separate memory cells set aside specifically for this purpose. Using the optimum input devices, the programmer can insert his instructions into the computer.

Most computers feature some means for storing often-encountered programs. In such cases, the programmer may receive a problem that has previously been solved. He simply locates the portion of the memory (which may be external to the computer) where the previously successful program has been stored and causes it to be transferred to the appropriate location for conducting the current program.

TYPICAL PROBLEM AND PROGRAM

Let us consider a step-by-step program for the simple problem mentioned previously, $y = ab + ac$. Assuming manual entry of data and instructions or commands (for example, using a digit-at-a-time keyboard), the programmer begins by pressing a key that clears the machine and removes any stored information that may be left over from previous problems. He then presses a key that tells the computer that he is about to enter data.

This primes his machine for action. Normally, he then presses a key (or keys) that identifies a particular storage location or *address* within the machine. Following this addressing, he inserts his first data, in this case, the value for *a*, which may consist of any number of digits, depending on the capacity of the storage location he has addressed. He then presses a key that causes the data to be shifted into the selected location.

In two similar steps, addressing different storage locations, he enters values for *b* and *c*. All the required *data* have now been entered, and the programmer must tell the computer what to do with the data.

To do this, he presses a key that tells the computer that he is about to enter instructions or commands. In his instructions, he selects symbols that initiate internally stored subprograms when necessary. For example, he says, take the data stored in address 0001 (the value for *a* in this case), multiply them by the data stored in address 0002 (the value for *b*), and store the resulting product in address 0004. His next command is take the data stored in address 0001, multiply them by the data stored in 0003 (the value for c), and store the resulting product in address 0005. Next he commands the machine to take the data from address 0004, add this number to that in 0005, and apply the result to an output register or storage location from which the value of y can be automatically typed out on the keyboard.

Finally, having stored all his data and instructions, he presses a key that instructs the computer to follow its commands in sequential order. When the computation is finished the results appear as specified (see Fig. 4–3).

The above problem, by itself, would be somewhat impractical for computer solution. The time required to enter the data and instructions would be many, many times greater than that required for the actual computation. Because only two multiplications and one addition are involved, the result would be available before the programmer could lift his finger from the key that initiated the computation.

Most computers have means for storing subprograms or subroutines internally, thus enabling the operator to call for a multiplication with one code, in spite of the fact that

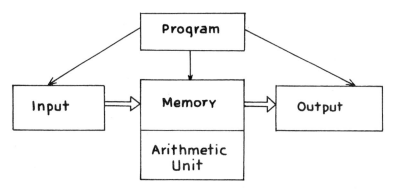

Fig. 4–3. It is the job of the digital-computer programmer to map the best route for his computer to follow in solving a problem. He chooses this route based on the relative importance of speed, quantity of computation, equipment available, and many other factors.

many steps are involved. The computer has the facility for following such subroutines when commanded to do so and, upon completion, to consult the program commands for a subsequent instruction.

TYPES OF PROGRAMS

The above example is greatly simplified to illustrate the step-by-step nature of a computer program. In a one-time program, it may not be practical for the programmer to spend much time refining his program for maximum efficiency. But in applications where a given program must be repeated over and over again, sometimes called a *production program*, it pays to have the programmer spend any time that is necessary to obtain peak efficiency.

Programs are usually "written" on prepared forms, which aid the programmer in developing a methodical routine. On such forms, spaces are provided for data, instructions or commands, and addresses (see Fig. 4–4). In most data-processing applications, data and commands are inserted at different points and usually by different types of input devices.

In many computer installations, computer users follow what is called an *open-shop* policy. The computer is available to a number of users, each of whom does his own programming. In such cases, all users cannot be expected to be experts at programming. Accordingly, most computer manufacturers make provisions for operating the computer with a simplified set of commands that can be understood by any reasonably well-educated user with only limited experience and training.

The Bendix G–15 has such a system, called Intercom 1000. Before operating the computer with this feature, the potential user transfers into the computer's memory, simply by inserting a roll of perforated paper tape, a series of translation instructions that convert the basic commands into ma-

Step No.	Data Source	Instruction or Command	Result Destination
1	Input (a)	Store	0001 0002
2	" (b)	"	0003
3	" (c)	"	
4			
5			
6			
7			
8			
9			
10			
11			
12			
13			
14			
15			
16			
17			
18			
19			
20			

Fig. 4–4.   The programmer arranges the various steps in his program in sequential order on prepared forms that can later be used to convert the "paper program" into machine language for absorption by the computer. Each type of computer uses a specially prepared form for this purpose.

chine commands. Each time the user employs one of the simplified commands in his program, the machine "looks up" the more sophisticated commands and executes the required operations. This particular machine also features a technique called POGO, which automatically converts an Intercom 1000 program into a highly efficient machine-language program for production-type computation.

Because the Bendix G–15 computer is typical of modern "small" digital computers, let us go into an examination of some of its features and see how they affect programming.

Data and commands can be inserted by means of a keyboard, which also serves as an output device. Both data and commands can also be inserted on perforated tape on the basic machine and on magnetic tape using a tape machine optionally available. All data and instructions are stored on a magnetic drum. Once a program has been run, it can be transferred to paper or magnetic tape for permanent storage.

So this, like other machines, has considerable flexibility. Combined inputs and output of keyboard, perforated tape, and magnetic tape can be used. In addition, provisions are made for entering the computer from any other digital source that is capable of activating the machine with the correct input signals.

The programmer must know these capabilities. Certain portions of his storage facilities are more accessible than others. Some functions can be carried on simultaneously with others, and if the programmer is thoroughly familiar with these, he can save time and greatly increase the operating efficiency of his installation.

FIXED-PROGRAM COMPUTERS

There are many digital computers in the field which have programs "wired in," that is, they are intended for a specific application involving the processing of data in accordance with a fixed or semifixed routine that eliminates the need for elaborate and flexible programming provisions. In such cases, extra attention to the input and output equipment is often required.

An example of the latter type of application is the equipment currently in use by many airlines and some railroads.

Similar systems have been installed and are being installed in increasing numbers by banks.

In the airline case, each ticket agent is, in effect, a computer programmer. He may know nothing of the computer's capabilities, but he may use it many times a day. In a typical case, the agent has a desk set which serves as an input device to the computer. He inserts a coded ticket into his desk set which may contain such information as flight number, the particular leg of the flight that is of interest to the customer, and other pertinent information. He then presses a key on a keyboard which asks the computer whether or not the potential passenger can buy three tickets. The fixed information identifies a computer storage location from which the machine withdraws a number corresponding to the number of tickets already sold for that flight. Comparing that number with the seating capacity of the airplane, the computer tells the agent that he can sell the tickets and automatically updates its memory to show the new figures. Many other types of data pertaining to the transaction are handled by computer also.

Because of the high speed of operation, the computer decreases customer waiting time, enables fewer people to do an efficient job of scheduling, and goes a long way toward eliminating customer ill will resulting from human errors. Many agents can have access to the complete reservation file almost immediately.

PAYROLL COMPUTATION

Thus it is seen that programming techniques can differ widely, depending primarily on the application. One of the most-common applications of high-speed digital computers is that of processing payrolls. This procedure involves relatively simple mathematical manipulations, but in large companies the quantity of work required is likely to be beyond the capabilities of even the largest payroll staff.

In such an application, the degree to which the process can be automatized depends on the type and quantity of computation equipment employed. Some of the data that must be entered into the active computer memory system might include worker's badge number, pay received to date, number of dependents, regular hours worked, overtime hours, hourly rate, insurance deductions, savings bond deductions, and, in some cases, credit union deductions. These data may be inserted by means of punch cards, keyboards, perforated paper tape, or magnetic tape.

Upon completion of the computation process, the following information must be made available: badge number, revised-year-to-date pay, gross pay, amount withheld for income tax, social security, insurance, bond and credit union deductions, and net pay.

Computations will vary, depending on the company's requirements. The program, which would be semifixed and stored in the program portion of the machine, would use the following route: (1) clear the system of previous data; (2) assign such constants as number of dependents, deductions, hourly rate, etc.; (3) assign memory cells to such variable data as hours of straight time and overtime and special deductions. This data input is completed in less than a second in most systems, and the computation can proceed.

The first step in the computation might be to withdraw the worker's badge number from its storage cell and cause it to be transferred to the output device. His earnings to date for the year might be printed out. His weekly gross computation can then be initiated as follows: The previously stored hourly rate is transferred from its memory cell to the arithmetic unit in a position where it can be multiplied by the number of hours straight time that is obtained from another memory cell. The appropriate overtime rate is calculated and transferred to another memory cell. The number of overtime hours and the resulting overtime rate are multiplied. The two products (straight time and overtime pay) are added to determine the worker's gross pay. The computer then interrogates memory cells that contain deductions and makes appropriate subtractions from the gross pay. The worker's net pay is printed out, along with his new earnings to date.

Output equipment may vary from system to system. In most cases, a tape or punch card is produced that is capable of activating printing equipment that actually prints out the worker's pay check, together with records for accounting and for computation of other records (such as money to be paid to the government for bonds and income taxes).

Once the computer has been programmed to follow the route described above, input data consist only of the items mentioned previously. The computer proceeds automatically from one worker's computation to the next until the payroll is completed.

ALTERNATIVE APPROACH

The problem of calculating some deductions is somewhat more complicated than indicated above. For example, formulas can be written to calculate withholding tax, but in some cases it is more efficient to prepare tables that can simplify and speed computation. The tabular approach has advantages where a finite number of possibilities exist. The computer assembles the criteria upon which results will be based, but instead of computing the result, the machine consults an electronic table that has previously been worked out for all possible combinations of criteria. The result is then available almost immediately.

When results are stored in tabular form, the computer actually decides on the appropriate address in the memory system. The result will be stored there, and the computer knows this because it has been instructed accordingly.

SOLVING SCIENTIFIC PROBLEMS

As a simple example of programming encountered in scientific work, the quadratic equation is typical. In such cases, an unknown quantity is contained in an equation, for example, $3x^2 + 5x - 2 = 0$. Because this equation contains the square of the unknown quantity, it is called a quadratic. Such equations are frequently encountered in engineering work.

The computer programmer looks at this problem in terms of a standard equation in which letters are substituted for the numbers. He sees the equation as $ax^2 + bx + c = 0$ where a, b, and c are called the *coefficients*. This form is called the *general quadratic* equation. The problem of solving such equations for the unknown quantity x is called *factoring*. To the trained mathematician the answer is often obvious by visual inspection, but more often the following formula is used to arrive at the solution:

$$x = \frac{-b \pm \sqrt{b^2 - 4ac}}{2a}$$

To arrive at a solution using a digital computer, values for a, b, and c are entered into selected memory cells. The program comprises the following steps: (1) Compute b^2 by multiplying the value b by itself and returning the result to another memory cell; (2) compute $-4ac$ by multiplying the product of a times c by 4 and return the result to another memory cell; (3) subtract $4ac$ from b^2 and initiate a square-root routine on the result (thus obtaining $\sqrt{b^2 - 4ac}$) and return the result to storage; (4) subtract the result from $-b$ (obtained from the original memory cell containing b) and store the result $-b - \sqrt{b^2 - 4ac}$; and (5) compute $2a$ and divide the previously obtained result by this result. From this computation one of the two possible values for x is obtained and printed out. By similar means the value $x = -b + \sqrt{b^2 - 4ac} / 2a$ is obtained for the other possible answer and the problem is complete.

Although the above problem may seem complex, results can be obtained in a matter of seconds. In a repetitive situation, the computer automatically clears itself after printing the results and accepts the next coefficients from the input device or the memory system.

Thus we see that computer programming is simply a matter of organizing the input data and causing the computer to perform computations on these data to achieve the desired result. Some programs require many months of preparation, others are immediately available in stored program machines. Computer programming is an art in itself. The competent computer programmer is very much in demand. Successful programming can mean the difference between success and failure of a computer installation.

· 5 ·

COMPUTER LOGIC CIRCUITRY

In the foregoing discussion of computer operations, many circuit functions have been taken for granted.
The need for certain types of decision elements was shown.
For example, the need often arises for a logic element that
can monitor two two-state conditions and determine which of
the four possible combinations of conditions exists.

BASIC LOGIC ELEMENTS

Such logic elements are called *gates*. One of the two
two-state signals being monitored is usually called the *controlling* function, the other the *controlled* function. In other
words, the controlling signal opens or closes the gate, and the
controlled signal passes through the gate if it is open and
does not if the gate is closed.

Because of the basic premise that digital computers work
on either *on* or *off* conditions, there can be little or preferably
no "in-between" outputs from gates. Under ideal conditions,
there would be no output if the input conditions were in such
combination as to prevent an output. But in actual operation,
a small output can occur when none is intended. Such spuri-

ous outputs are readily eliminated by subsequent circuitry, as will be shown.

THE AND GATE

Reviewing the requirements for the commonest logic circuit, the AND gate, the following table of conditions can be written. The two conditions x and y are the *input* conditions and z is the output condition required.

x	y	z
0	0	0
0	1	0
1	0	0
1	1	1

The symbolic representation of the above logic element is shown in Fig. 5–1. The table says that z will be a 1 if and only if both x *and* y are 1's.

The electrical conditions for 1's and 0's vary from computer to computer, depending on the type of components and

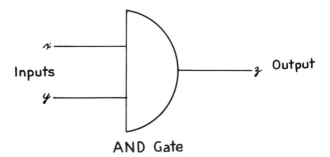

AND Gate

Fig. 5–1.   An AND gate has two inputs and one output. If *both* inputs are 1's, the output will be a 1. Under all other input conditions the output will be a 0. Inputs may be in the form of short duration pulses or continuous levels or combinations. The AND gate is the computer's most powerful single decision element.

circuitry used. However, for the purpose of explaining logic circuitry it is not necessary to distinguish one condition from the other as long as the *difference* between the two is recognized and retained.

THE OR GATE

The second-most-common computer-logic building block is the OR circuit, which is illustrated symbolically in Fig. 5–2 and whose function is summarized in the following table:

x	y	z
0	0	0
0	1	1
1	0	1
1	1	1

Note the difference in the z column. Here the table says that if either x or y is 1 (or both), z will be 1. Note also that the fact that both inputs are 1's is included as a condition for a 1 output. In certain instances, a gate is required that is truly an OR gate, that is, it will produce a 1 output if *either* input is 1,

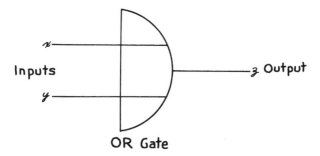

OR Gate

Fig. 5–2.   The OR gate, like the AND gate, has two inputs and one output. But the output will be a 1 if *either* or *both* of the inputs are 1's. A different type of OR gate produces a 1 output if and only if *either* input is a 1, excluding the situation in which both are 1's.

but not if *both* are 1's. This type of gate is referred to as an *exclusive* OR gate and is always specified as such. When not specified as an exclusive OR gate, it can be assumed that a normal gate is intended and that two 1's as inputs will produce an output of 1.

Combinations of AND and OR logic, together with flip-flops or some other kind of two-state storage device, comprise the bulk of any computer's circuitry. Fortunately, all these functions can readily be implemented electronically.

DIODES IN COMPUTER LOGIC

The basic principle upon which all logic circuits are based is the *nonlinearity* of certain electronic devices. More specifically, some devices exhibit a preference for passing current in one direction rather than in the opposite direction. Figure 5–3 shows a sketch and a symbolic diagram of a two-element vacuum tube called a *diode*. During its manufacture, the *cathode* of the diode is coated with a special material that has the property of "boiling off" electrons when heated. The *plate*, or *anode*, is a metallic sheet located some distance from the cathode. The *filament* is a thin wire through which current is passed (like the filament of an incandescent light bulb). The heat that results from the passage of current through the filament heats the cathode and causes it to boil off electrons whenever the filament is "lit."

It is a basic law of physics that similar electrical charges repel each other and that dissimilar charges attract each other. An electron is the basic *negative* (sometimes called *minus*) electrical charge. In a diode, electrons emitted by the cathode will be attracted to the plate when a positive voltage (referring to the cathode) is applied to the plate and will be repelled by the plate when its potential is negative (again with reference to the cathode).

In Fig. 5–4, two vacuum diodes are shown connected be-

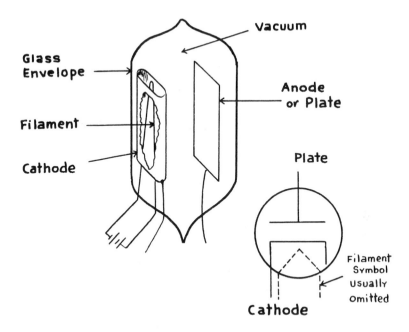

Fig. 5–3. Typical construction and electronic symbol for a vacuum diode. The thin wire filament heats the cathode, which in turn emits electrons. These electrons are attracted to the plate whenever it is at a positive potential with respect to the cathode. The diode acts as a "one-way" sign in electronic circuits, permitting current (electron) flow only under the above conditions and in only one direction.

tween voltage sources of opposite potential. Because the flow of electrons represents an electrical current, current will flow in (a) because the cathode (which emits electrons) is negative with respect to the plate. The relatively positive plate, being of opposite "charge" to the negative electrons, causes the negatively charged electrons to jump across the cathode to plate gap. In (b), no current will flow because the plate is negative with respect to the cathode. The plate cannot emit electrons, therefore, there are none available for current flow in the reverse direction.

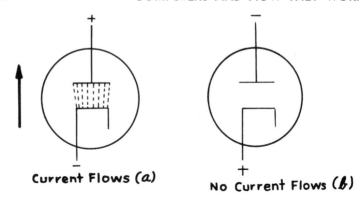

Fig. 5–4.   Simplified vacuum-diode symbols show the one-way nature of the operation. Current flows whenever the plate is positive with respect to the cathode. No current flows when the opposite condition prevails.

It is another basic law of physics that if an electron current passes through a circuit that resists the flow of the current (all circuits offer some resistance), part of the applied potential or voltage will appear across each resistance element in the circuit. The same law says that the voltage that appears across a resistance element will be proportional to the product of the current times the resistance. The basic units of *voltage, current,* and *resistance* related by this law are *volt, ampere,* and *ohm,* respectively. An ampere represents an amount of current seldom found in electronic logic circuits. However, the term *milliampere* (1/1000th ampere) is commonly used as a more practical way of defining electronic current magnitudes.

DIODE CIRCUITS

If a resistance is placed in series with the vacuum diodes illustrated in Fig. 5–4, as shown in Fig. 5–5, a voltage *drop* or change in potential will appear across the resistance in the

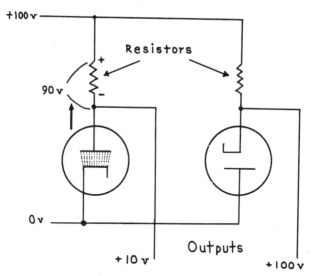

Fig. 5–5. A circuit showing two diodes with series resistors. A diode with a plate connected to positive voltage conducts and a voltage drop appears across its associated resistor. A diode connected in the reverse direction (cathode positive) does not conduct and no voltage drop appears across its series resistor.

circuit that is conducting current. But the resistance in the nonconducting circuit will have no voltage drop across it because the voltage across a resistance is proportional to both the current and the resistance, and the current is zero.

Notice that the top of the circuit in each case is at a voltage of 100 volts, and the bottom is at 0 volts. All voltages between these two points must be at intermediate levels. Although a theoretically perfect diode should offer no resistance in its *forward* (conducting) direction, all diodes offer some resistance to the flow of current. Let us assume that the conducting diode offers $\frac{1}{10}$ the resistance of its plate resistor. In this case, because the current is the same through both circuit elements (and voltage drop is proportional to resistance and current), $\frac{1}{10}$ of the total voltage will appear across the diode and the remaining $\frac{9}{10}$ (or 90 volts) will appear across the plate resistor. Therefore, the output voltage of the conducting circuit is 10 volts and the output voltage of the nonconducting circuit is the full 100 volts, all of which appears across the nonconducting diode since its resistance is infinite.

Notice that the vacuum diode in this type of circuit acts as a kind of one-way sign. It says that electron traffic can travel only from cathode to plate and, because the basic laws of physics dictate that electrons will pass from negative to positive, that the combination makes a logic device that transates polarity to current flow or no current flow. This phenomenon enables the computer to make decisions.

SEMICONDUCTOR DIODES

Although vacuum tubes once enjoyed an almost exclusive place in the electronic computer circuit, they recently have lost their popularity to *solid-state* devices such as *semiconductor diodes* and *transistors*. These offer better reliability and consume far less physical space and power plus many other advantages.

Figure 5–6 shows the logical equivalence of semiconductor diodes to vacuum-tube diodes. Normally, solid-state devices are operated at lower voltages, 3 to 20 volts being common. Like the vacuum diode, the semiconductor passes current in one direction, from the cat's whisker to the crystal. In a semiconductor diode, there may be some current flow in the undesired direction, but this will be slight in comparison with the desired direction. These directions are usually referred to as the *forward* and *reverse* directions, and the *forward current* (heavy) and the *reverse current* (extremely low, owing to the high resistance offered by the diode in the reverse direction).

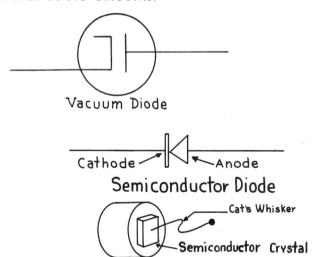

Vacuum Diode

Cathode ⟶ ◁ ⟵ Anode

Semiconductor Diode

Cat's Whisker

Semiconductor Crystal

Fig. 5–6. The sketches show the symbol for and construction of the increasingly popular semiconductor diode. Such diodes are extremely compact, require no filament power, and can be made relatively inexpensively. However, some current (although extremely small in high-quality units) can flow in the opposite direction.

LOGIC CIRCUITS

Let us now see how diodes can be used to perform digital logic functions. To begin with, consider the two-input AND circuit. Figure 5–7 shows schematically the way in which two diodes and a resistor can be used to perform the AND function. The component junction points of Fig. 5–7 are identified according to the convention used in the previous logic tables.

[At this point it should be understood that most computer designers have different ideas as to what shall constitute a logical 0 and what shall constitute a logical 1. Most frequently, in solid-state computers, 0 volts constitutes one condition (usually a logical 0), and a minus voltage of a few

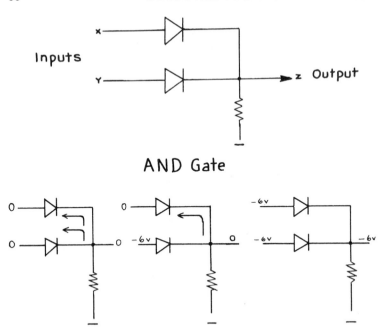

Fig. 5–7. A typical diode AND gate shows the use of two semiconductor diodes with a resistor connected to high (−18 volts or so) negative potential. Output will be −6 volts only if both inputs are −6 volts. Output will be 0 when either input (or both) is 0.

volts constitutes the opposite condition (usually a logical 1). For the purpose of explaining logic circuits, it will be helpful to adopt a pair of voltage levels and to assign them logical connotations. Unless otherwise specified, we shall use −6 volts as a logic 1 and 0 volts as a logic 0.]

Let us examine the four possibilities and see if the circuit shown in Fig. 5–7 fulfills the requirements for performing the AND function. The first case is one in which both inputs are 0's or 0 volts. Notice that the free end of the resistor is tied to a source of negative potential that is several times more negative than any possible input (−6 volts maximum). Because both inputs are 0 volts, both inputs are more positive than the negative bias voltage, and either or both diodes will conduct (their anodes are positive with respect to their cathodes). Because the voltage drop across conducting diodes is small, the output will essentially equal the inputs and will therefore be the required 0 volts for a logical 0.

If either input is a 1 (or —6 volts) and the other input is 0 (0 volts), the 0 input diode will be biased in its forward direction and current will flow through it, thus reducing the output voltage to 0 volts. The 1 input diode will not conduct current in this case, because its anode is —6 volts with respect to its cathode.

When both inputs are 1's (both —6 volts), either or both will conduct current, with the result that the output will be essentially equal to either input, or —6 volts.

Thus we have fulfilled the requirements of a *negative logic* AND gate. For a *positive logic* AND gate, we would simply reverse the diodes and use a positive bias voltage. The circuit shown will also function as an OR circuit, where any 0 input will result in a 0 output.

OR-GATE CIRCUITS

Figure 5–8 shows a two-input OR gate using two diodes and a resistor. The only differences between this and the AND circuit are the direction of the diodes and the polarity of the bias voltage. Referring to the OR-gate table, we see that two input 0's should cause a 0 output. If we apply 0 volts to x and y, current will flow in either or both diodes because their cathodes are negative with respect to their anodes. The voltage drop will thus be low, and the output will equal the input and be at the required 0 level.

If either x or y goes to —6 volts, representing a 1, the associated diode will conduct more current (because of the increased potential from —6 volts to the positive bias), and the voltage drop across it will be negligible. Thus the output

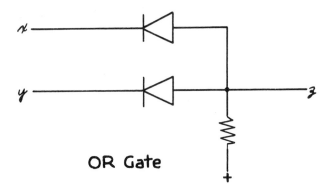

OR Gate

Fig. 5–8. A diode OR gate, similar to the AND gate shown in Fig. 5–7 except that diodes and voltage supply are reversed. The circuits in Figs. 5–7 and 5–8 are designed for logic using −6 volts as a 1 and 0 volts as a 0.

will equal the −6 volts required to signify a logic 1 output. The other diode will be cut off, since its cathode is positive with respect to its anode.

If both inputs are 1's (both at −6 volts), either or both will conduct sufficient current to reduce the output to −6 volts and thus create the required logic 1 output.

The vacuum-tube equivalents of these simple logic circuits can readily be drawn by substituting vacuum diodes, replacing the pointed part of the solid-state-device symbol with the tube plate or anode and the straight-line symbol with the tube cathode.

INVERTERS

One other important logic element is that which will provide a logical output that is opposite to its input. For example, applying a 1 to its input results in the appearance of a 0 at the output and vice versa.

Most modern electronic computers are replacing diode and tube logic with transistor logic. The transistor, a recent addition to the computer builder's bag of tricks, has several unique features that give it powers not formerly available in vacuum tubes and diodes.

TRANSISTOR CIRCUITS

Many different types of transistors are in use today, but basically they can be represented as shown in Fig. 5-9. The barriers between the three regions (*emitter, base,* and *collector*) act as diodes. That is, they conduct current readily in one direction but oppose it in the opposite direction. However, it is found that current flow between the base and

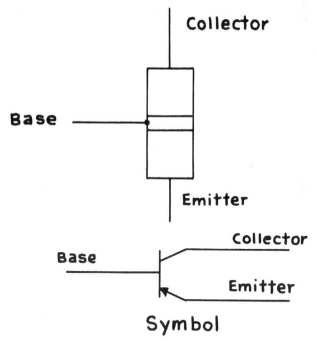

Fig. 5-9. The typical construction and electronic symbol for a transistor. The base region may be only a few thousandths of an inch thick. The arrow in the emitter symbol can be reversed for different types of transistors. Some transistors have four leads for special-purpose circuits.

emitter has an effect on the flow of collector current. The relationship is such that large quantities of collector current flow can be controlled by relatively small changes in base current, thus giving *amplification.*

Figure 5–10 shows a simple transistor circuit with the base used as an input and the collector as an output. The usual resistor appears in series with the collector and its voltage supply (which, in this case, is negative). If the base is made negative, emitter-base current is encouraged to flow because this is the forward direction for the diode formed by the emitter-base junction. The collector-base junction is biased in its reverse direction, but when emitter-base current flows, the normally high reverse resistance of the collector-base junction is lowered, and collector current flows. In an ideal transistor, the collector resistance is lowered to such a point that the current in the collector circuit is limited only by the collector resistor. Thus all the applied voltage appears

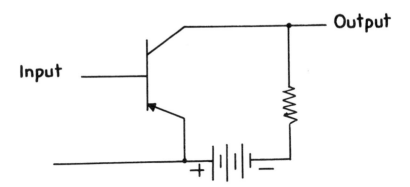

Fig. 5–10.   A simplified schematic drawing of a transistor amplifier. The voltage source (shown as a battery) is oriented in such a direction that the current flow is resisted by the emitter-collector circuit of the transistor until the base current is made to flow by the input circuit. The resulting collector-circuit current is an amplified version of the input (base) current.

across the collector resistor, and the output voltage drops to 0 volts.

When the base is made positive (or 0 volts), there is no encouragement for emitter-base current, with the result that collector current ceases to flow. Thus most of the supply voltage appears across the collector, and the output voltage rises toward the negative collector supply voltage (it would equal the collector supply voltage if current flow were cut off completely).

The transistor acts as a current switch in digital applications. Its collector resistance is extremely low when its base is negative and extremely high when its base is 0 or positive. To perform logic operations with transistors, we use them as current switches, as shown in Fig. 5–11. In the AND circuit two transistors are used in tandem. If both inputs are 1's (—6 volts, according to the previously adopted convention), both transistors will act as closed switches and the output will be at 0 volts. If either or both inputs become 0 or slightly positive, the corresponding transistor(s) will act like an open switch and the output will drop to a voltage level determined by the circuit constants.

NOR LOGIC

Another useful type of transistor circuit is the NOR gate. In this case, logic operations are performed at the input to the transistor, as shown in Fig. 5–12. Because of the ability of the transistor to amplify any small base current to a substantial collector current change, several inputs can be paralleled to the base. If any such input is at —6 volts, base current flows and the output voltage drops to 0 volts. If all inputs are 0 volts, base current is discouraged, collector current drops to zero, and the output voltage becomes negative. This type of circuit can be used as an OR circuit if 0 volts represents a logic 0 and a minus voltage represents a logic 1.

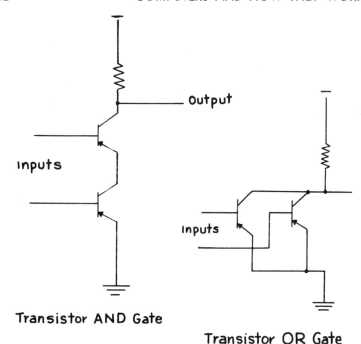

Transistor AND Gate

Transistor OR Gate

Fig. 5–11. Transistors lend themselves ideally to computer-type logic circuitry. The AND gate requires current bias of both inputs to permit flow of collector current. In a transistor OR gate, current in either base circuit will close the collector circuit.

It will be noted from the preceding discussion that outputs sometimes are inverted, that is, a logic 1 voltage level appears where a logic 0 level is desired and vice versa. This is often a useful feature. Where original conditions must be restored, or where an inversion of logic levels is required for some other purpose (as in the half-adder circuit described in Chapter 3), an inverting amplifier can be used. Figure 5–13 shows a typical transistor inverter. A negative input applied to the base encourages base current, causing collector current to flow and reducing the output to 0 volts. When the input is

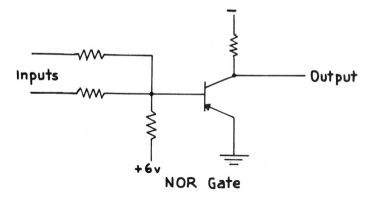

Fig. 5–12. A transistor logic circuit for which there is no vacuum-tube equivalent is the NOR circuit, which can accommodate a number of inputs, perform AND and OR logic functions, and uses only one transistor.

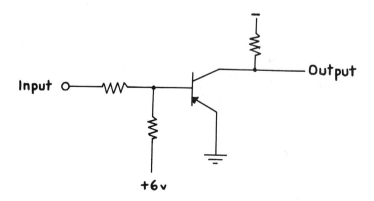

Fig. 5–13. In logic circuitry, it is often necessary to invert or reverse a logic condition (for example, in the half adder discussed in Chapter 3). The simple circuit shown serves this function. By proper choice of components, output can be made to be opposite (logically speaking) of input.

0 or slightly positive, collector current is cut off (because base current does not flow) and the output becomes negative.

CLAMPING

We have also mentioned above that a negative output level is determined by circuit constants. Because circuit constants are subject to change with the life of components and because digital circuits operating between two well-defined levels are most desirable, a process called *clamping* is frequently used.

For example, consider Fig. 5–14, which is similar to Fig. 5–13 except that another voltage source and a diode have been added. Assuming ideal components, the collector resistance becomes infinite when the base is made 0 or positive. In

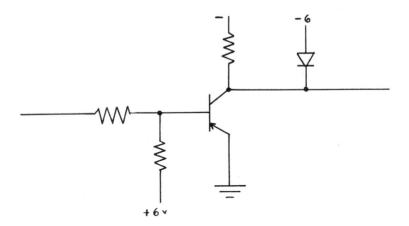

Fig. 5–14. Clamping is used in most practical logic circuits to ensure uniformity of logic voltage levels. When the transistor shown above conducts, its collector resistance is so low that the output is essentially 0 volts. When it is nonconducting, the clamping diode has its anode positive and offers very low resistance. This results in an output equal to the −6-volt supply voltage, which may be maintained as accurately as necessary.

this case, the transistor can essentially be removed from the circuit, so that only the two voltage supplies and the diode remain. Because the anode of the diode is positive with respect to its cathode, the diode will conduct. Again assuming a perfect diode, its resistance becomes zero and no voltage drop appears across it. Thus the output voltage equals the voltage applied to its anode, or exactly —6 volts. If the transistor input is negative, the transistor collector circuit can be assumed to have negligible resistance; thus the collector voltage equals the emitter voltage or 0 volts. In this way, the two desired voltage levels are preserved.

NPN VERSUS PNP TRANSISTORS

There are actually two distinct types of transistors. These are called *NPN* and *PNP*. The NPN transistor requires that its collector be biased positively, and a positive base voltage causes collector current flow. The PNP transistor, which has been used in the previous examples, requires a negative collector supply voltage, and a negative base voltage causes collector current flow. The PNP transistor might be likened to a vacuum tube that passes electrons from plate to cathode. Advantage is often taken of the availability of these two complementary types of transistors.

FLIP-FLOP CIRCUITS

Thus far we have seen how tubes, diodes, and transistors can be used to perform gating functions. They can also be used as storage devices, or *flip-flops*. Figure 5–15 shows a simple transistor flip-flop. This circuit is an adaptation of a tube circuit that was developed by two electronics pioneers named Eccles and Jordan, and it bears their name.

The two transistors are connected in such a way that if one is conducting the other is cut off, and vice versa. For ex-

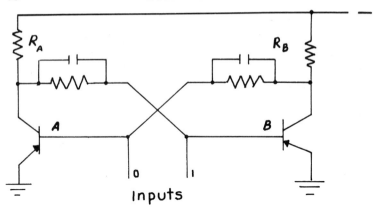

Fig. 5–15. A basic transistor flip-flop circuit. The conduction of transistor A causes a voltage drop across R_A, which is applied to the base of
transistor B, keeping it cut off. Absence of current through R_B causes
the collector of transistor B to be near supply potential, holding the
base of transistor A in conducting condition. A negative pulse to the
cutoff transistor causes conditions to reverse (as in the case of a push on
the high side of a seesaw described in Chapter 2).

ample, if transistor A is conducting, heavy collector current
flows and the collector of A approaches 0 volts. Because this
voltage is applied directly to the base of transistor B, the base
current of that transistor is very low, with the result that its
collector current is essentially cut off. We can assign either a
logical 1 or a logical 0 to this condition as long as we reserve
the opposite assignment for the opposite condition.

To reverse the condition of the transistor flip-flop we
simply ground the base of the conducting transistor momentarily. This cuts off the conducting transistor's collector current and thus causes its collector voltage to rise sharply in the
negative direction. This voltage rise is applied to the base of
the transistor that was cut off, causing its base to conduct. As
a result, collector current flows, its collector voltage drops toward 0 volts, and the previously conducting transistor's base
is held at ground potential even after the momentary ground
is removed.

Flip-flops are made as symmetrical as possible, so they assume random conditions when power is first applied. Before being entrusted to the storage of logical conditions, flip-flops are usually reset to an arbitrary starting point. A separate *reset* input is often provided specifically for this purpose.

In actual computer use, flip-flops are *triggered* by the application of voltage pulses because these can be generated electronically much faster than a point can be grounded. The effect may be the same if a voltage is momentarily reduced to 0 volts or ground potential.

Outputs from flip-flops are normally obtained from the transistor collector circuit. Either a negative-going or a positive-going voltage can be obtained simply by connecting the flip-flop to the appropriate collector (one will be going *up* when the other is going *down,* and vice versa).

PRACTICAL CIRCUITS

There are literally thousands of different types of logic circuits, all of which in practice are somewhat more complex than the simple flip-flops illustrated above. Additions are made to improve speed and reliability of switching. A typical general-purpose circuit is shown in Fig. 5–16. Such circuits are packaged by a number of manufacturers for use in building up computer logic systems. A typical package housing a complete flip-flop is shown in Fig. 5–17. Other logic circuits, packaged similarly, permit fabrication of logic systems; these have plain wires to interconnect the logic packages in the desired combination.

BINARY COUNTING

To illustrate a typical logic system comprised of transistor flip-flops, let us assume that we require a binary counter

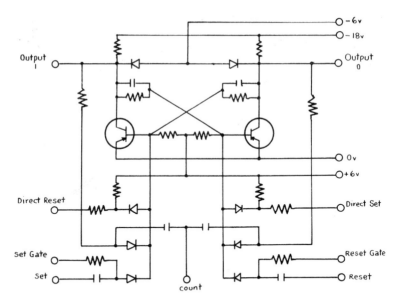

Fig. 5–16. A schematic drawing of a commercial general-purpose transistor flip-flop featuring several methods of setting and resetting. Note the use of −6-volt diode clamps on the collector outputs to maintain logic levels of approximately 0 and −6 volts. A pulse applied to the count terminal will cause the circuit to reverse, regardless of the starting condition.

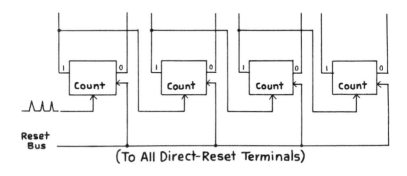

Fig. 5–17. A simple block diagram of a four-stage binary counter having a count capacity of sixteen (including 0 as a number). Boxes are flip-flops similar to the one shown in Fig. 5–16. Counters of this type can count as many as several million pulses per second.

that is capable of counting up to 15 (or 16 if a count of zero is included as a number). For this purpose, four flip-flops are required. All must be reset to their 0 states prior to the beginning of a count. This is achieved by the application of a pulse to the common reset bus.

After all stages have been reset to their 0 condition, the *first pulse* is applied to the input of the first stage, switching its condition from 0 to 1. This input is arranged so that the application of a negative-going voltage to the terminal will cause the circuit to switch.

The left-hand collector of each stage is connected to the counter input of the succeeding stage. When the first pulse is applied, the collector goes positive. But the succeeding stage will be switched only if a negative-going pulse is applied to its counter input, so nothing will happen to the second stage or to succeeding stages.

Upon the arrival of the *second pulse*, the first stage again switches, resuming its 0 state. In so doing, the left-hand collector goes negative and this negative-going voltage change causes the second stage to turn on. The *third pulse* again sets the first stage to its 1 state, but the left-hand collector of the first stage again goes positive and the succeeding stages are unaffected. Thus the counter stores a count of 3 by having its two least-significant stages turned on, as required in the normal binary-count progression. The *fourth pulse* again turns off the first stage (returns it to its 0 condition). In turning off, the left-hand collector goes negative, and as a result the second stage is switched also. Having been in its 1 state, the second stage resumes its 0 condition; in so doing, its left-hand collector goes negative, switching the third stage to its 1 condition.

This count progression proceeds until, after the application of fifteen input pulses, all stages are on or in their 1 states. Looking at the four stages symbolically, we have the number 1111 stored, which is the binary number for 15. A sixteenth pulse returns all stages to their 0 states. If a fifth stage is added, using the left-hand collector of the fourth stage as its input, the counter will have a count capacity of 32 (including zero as a number), and so on.

Through the use of special *feedback* circuits, the same type of counter elements can be used in binary-coded decimal counters. In this case, the elements are arranged in groups of four. Each time one of these sets of four elements receives its tenth input signal, the feedback circuits cause a pulse to be applied to the next most-significant group. All stages are automatically returned to their 0 states by a "brute-force" method; this prevents interaction among stages within the group because off-going voltages are connected to subsequent stages.

· 6 ·

HOW MEN AND MACHINES COMMUNICATE

Much of today's computer research goes toward the development of new and better methods of filling the gap between man and machine. Man must make his wishes known to the computer, and the computer must present its results in a form that is useful to its operator.

Modern computers can accept information in a variety of ways. In order for man to enter his numbers and instructions into the computer, he must first translate his problems into computer language in a form that the machine can accept.

INPUT INFORMATION

Regardless of the method of entry, two types of information must be furnished to the computer: the *data to be processed* and *commands* or *instructions* that tell the computer what to do with the data put in. Commands form the basis of the program and may vary in quantity and complexity, depending on the type of problem being solved and the computer being used. Many methods of program entry are used (see Fig. 6–1).

Input data can also be applied in a variety of ways. In scientific problems, where the amount of input data may be small in comparison with the program, manual keyboard input of data may provide sufficient speed. In most data-processing applications, however, the amount of data to be processed may be voluminous, precluding the use of such slow input devices as the character-at-a-time keyboard.

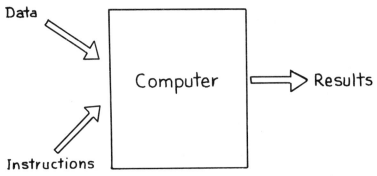

Fig. 6–1. Two types of input information must be fed to the computer: (1) data to be processed, and (2) instructions or commands that tell the computer what to do with the data. Methods of entering each type of information can be the same or different, depending upon the problem and the computer involved.

In most computers (and there are exceptions), the time required to insert data and instructions detracts from the computer's actual production time. The slower the input device, the less efficient the installation, and the higher the cost per problem.

INPUT PREPARATION

To avoid this, input data can be translated into a form that can be assimilated by the computer at its optimum information rate. In some instances, this will represent a slow-down and in some cases a speeding up of information. A typical example of a way to speed up data translation would be the change from a manual (character-at-a-time) keyboard to perforated or magnetic tape (see Fig. 6–2). A skilled operator can punch several characters a second on a keyboard. Once the tape is prepared in this manner, however, it can be read into the computer at rates as high as 1000 characters per second (perforated tape), or up to several tens of thousands of characters per second (magnetic tape).

Fig. 6–2. Some computers use the same device for input and output. Typical is the Bendix G–15, which uses the typewriter keyboard shown. An optional output device, where appropriate, is the x–y plotter on the right side of the operator's desk. At the left in the background are two magnetic-tape machines used for high-volume medium-fast-access storage.

The use of peripheral equipment to prepare information for computer entry is referred to as an *off-line* operation (see Fig. 6–3). The computer is not involved, although the equipment used may at some other time be connected directly to the computer to act as an input or output device. A card punch, for example, can be used in a tape-to-card converter and later be used with the computer as a card output or input device. In the former case, the punch is acting as an off-line punch, but when used with the computer its function becomes on-line.

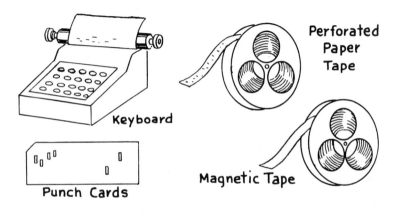

Fig. 6–3. Typical computer input devices include a keyboard similar to a standard electric typewriter and punch cards, perforated paper tape, and magnetic tape, usually prepared off-line by peripheral equipment. Input devices are shown in ascending order of speed capabilities.

COMPUTER ENTRY

Before going into further detail on the transfer of information into and out of the digital computer, let us take a look at the portion of the computer with which we want to communicate. Every computer has one or more main entrances. Each piece of information arriving at the front gate is assigned a particular memory cell or register, where it will stay until called for during the computation.

The input-output equipment corresponds to the transportation systems that bring the information to the main entrance and convey it away from the main entrance when the game is over.

In most modern computers, several bits of input information arrive at the entrance simultaneously, their combination representing codes that specify certain numbers or letters or instructions. In a machine that accepts a character at a time, each character is ushered to its particular memory cell, often within microseconds after the input equipment presents it at the input gate. Some machines have a waiting room in the form of a multiple-character *input register*, or *buffer*, which is filled a character at a time by the input device. Once filled, its contents are transferred simultaneously to appropriate memory cells.

Several different types of memory cells will be discussed in Chapter 7, but for the purpose of discussing input-output equipment, it is necessary only to think of these cells as two-state devices, the states of which can be adjusted by input data.

DATA-INPUT EXAMPLE

As a basic example of how and why data must be transferred from point to point in an electronic computer or data-processing system, let us consider a familiar computation, the U.S. Federal income tax.

Throughout the year, the taxpayer accumulates income, usually at a regular weekly or monthly rate, but possibly in differing amounts and sometimes from different sources. He spends part of his income on nontaxable commodities, and his employer withholds some of his earnings to pay his taxes, according to Federal law.

At the end of the year, the taxpayer finds himself faced with a relatively difficult computation. A mathematical formula for such a computation would be fantastically complicated because of the almost unlimited number of unusual circumstances that arise because of the unique situation of each taxpayer. As a result, the Bureau of Internal Revenue prepares a form to assist the taxpayer in computing his tax.

The *instructions* on the form are identical with the *program* of an electronic computer.

The *spaces* provided for the various pieces of information required for the computation are the same as the computer's *memory cells.*

The *information* placed in the spaces corresponds to the *input data.*

The taxpayer's *pen* or *typewriter* is the *input device.* (His pen may also be the output device if when the computation is complete the results show that he owes more money.)

The blank sheet of paper provided with some tax forms might be compared to the computer's arithmetic unit, in which the actual computations are carried on.

Taking an extremely simple case to see how the electronic computer might handle an income tax computation, the input data would be arranged and presented in such a way that dollars and cents could be inserted in any prescribed storage register or memory cell. In addition, the computer must be capable of accepting alphabetic information to convey the taxpayer's name, address, employer, and other information involving letters of the alphabet as well as numeric digits.

The input information is prepared in computer language, using the most-convenient peripheral equipment. A keyboard-operated punch could be used to prepare punch cards with the desired input data. These cards are then inserted in the computer's card reader, and the appropriate program (in this case the set of instructions) is selected and placed in action (see Fig. 6–3).

INSTRUCTION ENTRY

By prearrangement, the data is presented in the proper sequence. The program calls for the input device to transfer the first block of characters into storage register 1, which corresponds to the space reserved for the taxpayer's name. The next set of characters is transferred to the space for the address, and so on, until all input data, including income, withholding, medical expenses, contributions, and other information have been inserted into their assigned storage locations.

At the conclusion of this memory-filling phase, actual computation can begin. The program instructs the computer to withdraw the income numbers from storage one at a time and to add them to determine total income. This result is returned to a selected storage location.

The program then calls for deductions, and the computer again adds to determine the total and returns it to storage. The sequence proceeds until the final result appears in the answer register.

At this point, it is only important to recognize the importance of being able to transfer data from external sources into selected memory cells of the computer. The timing of data transfers may differ from computer to computer, and data may be fed into the machine in small or large quantities. In all cases, however, the data enter at one point and must be physically transferred within the computer to selected storage locations. It will be helpful in understanding input-output devices to look ahead momentarily and see what happens to data once they are presented at the threshold of the computer.

DIGITAL INPUT CIRCUITS

We have seen how a number of 0 through 9 can be described by four bits of information in the form of *on* or *off* bits (1's and 0's). If we had four two-position switches, as shown in Fig. 6–4, we could readily define any four-bit numeric digit by placing the switches in the appropriate positions and looking at the remote ends of the four wires connected to the switches. Arbitrarily we say that any line that shows —6 volts will be considered a 1, and any line that shows 0 volts, a 0.

Computer *registers* are comprised of a number of two-state devices, each of which can have its condition *changed* remotely and have its condition *sampled* or *sensed* remotely. The register is a temporary resting place for data, but it is capable of retaining information entrusted to it until it is purposely reset by the computer program. Like the seesaw

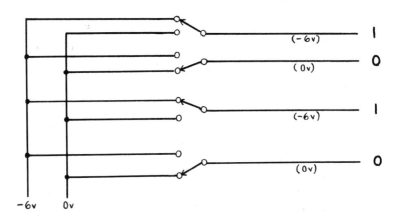

Fig. 6–4.   Four two-position toggle switches permit remote transmission of four-bit binary-coded decimal information. Arbitrarily, we say that switches in the —6-volt position signify 1, and 0-volt positions signify 0. The voltmeter at the far end of the four wires can detect a remote information code.

whose condition was maintained by the effect of gravity on the bowling ball, the storage-register element retains its condition electrically. It changes its condition when a momentary electrical impulse is applied to the proper terminal (like a momentary push on the "up" side of the seesaw). Some electronic register elements can have their states change in small fractions of millionths of seconds.

INPUT BY ELECTRICAL IMPULSES

When it is desired to store information in a computer register (which is the goal of all computer input devices), electrical pulses are routed (by wires) to appropriate terminals of the individual storage elements that comprise the register. Flip-flop storage elements are normally symmetrical, both physically and electrically. One input is provided for each "side" in such a way that the condition of the circuit depends on which input is pulsed.

Let us here adopt a practical convention and say that if a potential of —6 volts is momentarily applied to the 1 terminal of a storage element, the element will turn *on* and store a 1 bit. Application of —6 volts to the 0 terminal will similarly cause the element to turn *off* and store a 0 bit.

To store a four-bit number in one digit position of a computer register it is necessary to apply negative voltage pulses to appropriate sides of the corresponding elements. This could be achieved by the simple circuit shown in Fig. 6–5, where the two-position switches determine the routing of the pulses resulting from the closing of the "load" switch. Unfortunately, this scheme requires two wires for each storage element.

If we start the loading process with all stages in the 0 condition, only 1's pulses need be routed. This can be accomplished as illustrated in Fig. 6–6. Just prior to loading, all elements are set to their 0 condition by momentarily closing

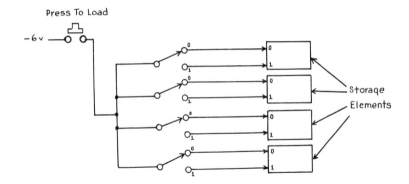

Fig. 6–5. Typical storage elements are set to the 1 or 0 conditions by application of a momentary −6-volt potential to the appropriate "side." Toggle switches do the necessary routing and the push button facilitates a momentary −6-volt pulse. Notice that eight lines are required to transmit four bits from the toggle switches to the storage elements.

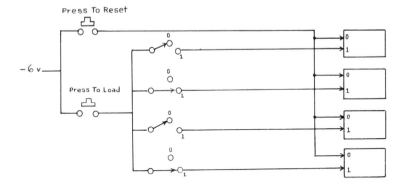

Fig. 6–6. By setting all storage elements to a common condition before transmitting information to them, one line per bit can be used between switches and storage elements. In the case shown, all elements are set to 0 by application of a −6-volt signal to all 0 inputs. During load, −6-volt pulses are routed to 1 inputs of all storage elements that are to store 1's. Others are left in the 0 state.

the "reset" switch. Then with four wires and four simple on-off switches, the desired setting of *on* elements can be achieved.

To store another digit in another digit position of the register, the four wires must be transferred to the *on* sides of the next set of storage elements, the input switches changed to match the new code to be stored, and the "load" switch closed to initiate the negative electrical impulse that sets the 1's elements. The wire switching can be achieved electronically at very high rates of speed to enable information to be distributed into large registers in very short periods of time.

With such electronic distributors to switch between data storage locations, the limiting factor in the scheme illustrated above is the time required to set the switches according to the input codes. Some types of manual keyboards give appropriate switch combinations when the operator presses a single key. But even this is slow in data-processing situations in which most of the time is consumed in entering data. In such cases, faster data-entry rates are almost essential.

PERFORATED-TAPE INPUT DEVICES

Paper tape, with coded holes and no-holes, can serve the same function as the keyboard and its operator. Of course, the tape must be prepared, possibly by the same operator and keyboard (together with a tape punch), but once prepared the tapes may be read at high speeds, thus reducing computer time consumed in entering data.

Because of the wide variety of codes and applications, an equally wide variety of perforated tape and handling equipment is available for computer usage. Some perforated tapes are made of mylar plastic material, and others are made in the form of a sandwich, aluminum or paper between two thin films of plastic material. Some are made of plain paper in various colors, some opaque and some translucent. Tapes that have five, six, seven, and eight levels, or rows (plus a row of small *sprocket* holes), are commonly used. In most systems, the holes are punched through the tape, but some systems employ equipment that "indents" holes, the "hole" here being a depression in the body of the tape. In all cases, however, information is contained in the coding of holes and no-holes. Usually in perforated-tape systems each column of hole positions across the tape (perpendicular to its length) represents a binary-coded character.

Holes are punched mechanically by machines that operate at speeds that permit the punching of only a few characters per second or as many as 240 characters per second (see Fig. 6–7). The perforator may be connected electrically or mechanically to a keyboard in such a way that when the operator presses one of the keys, the corresponding digital code is automatically punched in the next available digit position of the tape. If the operator presses the number seven key, for example, the punches in rows one, two, and three are activated, the punches in all other rows are inhibited. Thus assigning the binary weights to the rows, as discussed in

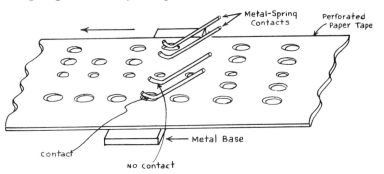

Fig. 6–7. A typical commercial paper-tape perforator. Digital codes are applied to input terminals and selected punches place holes in 1 positions. The punch shown can operate at character rates as high as sixty per second. *(Courtesy Tally Register Corp.)*

Chapter 5, the seven has been coded and recorded on the tape. As the punches withdraw from their dies, an electro-mechanical device brings the next column (digit position) into location for punching, and the system is ready for the oper-ator's next move.

PAPER-TAPE READERS

Now let us consider the problem of reading perforated tape. A simple (though not too practical) device for achieving this task is that illustrated in Fig. 6–8. As the tape is passed through the reading mechanism, electrical contact is made through the tape at positions containing holes. The electrical insulation offered by the tape at no-hole locations creates the opposite condition (no contact) from that at hole locations (contact). Thus the function of the toggle switches illustrated in Fig. 6–8 has been automated. The characters are being translated into an electrical language that the computer can understand and use to set its internal storage elements, pro-

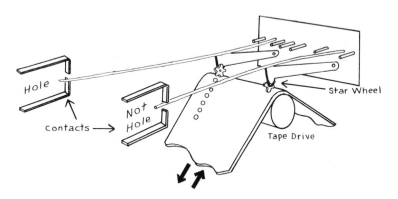

Fig. 6–8.   To speed sequencing of input codes, perforated paper tape is often employed. Contacts made through holes indicating 1 bits can be substituted for the toggle switches shown in Fig. 6–6 to obtain automatic setting of storage elements.

viding that the necessary requirements for talking to the machine exist.

The crude system illustrated in Fig. 6–8 is in use today in some types of tape readers, but it has some weaknesses. It is vulnerable to fuzz, which can prevent or delay contact and cause missing of a hole, and it is hard on tape, a factor that is not always important but can be of grave consequence in some applications.

Another type of reader is shown in Fig. 6–9. Here star-shaped wheels are aligned with the tape rows. The star wheels are held against the tape by a spring. The physical dimensions of the wheels are such that when the wheel encounters a hole, the leading tooth (as the tape is moved past the wheels) rotates into the hole, lowering the arm connected to it and changing the contact from upper to lower (like moving the two-position toggle switch). If the next column contains another hole for the same row, the contact remains in the lower position. When a no-hole appears, the star wheel

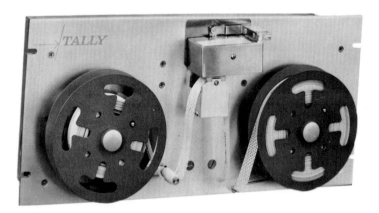

Fig. 6–9. An improved form of paper-tape reader uses *star* wheels whose points mesh with holes, or slide along paper tape where no holes exist. Mechanical linkage provides double-throw switch action for remote determination of 1's and 0's.

again assumes its position of sliding along the surface of the
tape where it remains until another hole appears. With this
system, the circuit designer has a choice of two conditions
(switch closed or switch open) for 1's and 0's.

Both reading systems described are limited in speed.
They are highly practical for character-reading rates of sixty
per second or so, but when higher speeds are desired, electronic methods are employed.

PHOTOELECTRIC PAPER-TAPE READERS

Figure 6–10 illustrates the increasingly popular photoelectric perforated-tape reader. Taking advantage of the
opacity of the tape, a lamp is placed on one side of the tape,
and photosensitive detectors, one for each row, are placed on
the opposite side. The stored 1's and 0's are determined by
the detectors, which see light or no light depending on
whether a hole or a no-hole is at a particular spot on the tape.

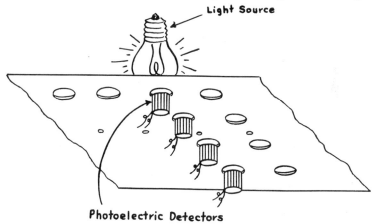

Light Source

Photoelectric Detectors

Fig. 6–10.   A greatly increased speed of reading perforated paper tape
is made possible by photoelectric detection of holes and no-holes. Electronic amplifiers raise the voltage levels generated by photoelectric detectors to levels useful in logic circuits.

The photocell signals obtained in this mannner are of little use to a computer without amplification. The amplifiers required for photoelectric reading make photoelectric readers more expensive than mechanical readers. As usual, a price is paid for greater speed and flexibility.

One important feature of perforated-tape system is the ability to start and stop at will and to operate synchronously (at some regular or periodic rate) or asynchronously (at any random rate or combination of random and periodic rates). The slower machines have little difficulty in fulfilling this requirement because their advancement is normally initiated by application of an electrical impulse to an electromechanical device that advances the tape a distance corresponding to the distance between two adjacent sprocket holes. When higher speeds are involved, however, the sprocket holes cannot be used in this manner because the tape is not strong enough to withstand the concentrated force that would have to be applied to accelerate and decelerate in one period of the reading rate.

To circumvent this difficulty, high-speed machines use a system of capstans and pinch rollers. The capstan is turned at high speed by a motor. The tape is advanced when an electrically activated pinch roller presses the tape against the capstan. More details on this subject will be presented in connection with the discussion of magnetic-tape-handling equipment.

A perforated tape containing input information will sometimes also contain certain instructions pertaining to the feeding of information into the computer. For example, one combination of holes and no-holes (a combination not used to define input data) can conveniently be used to halt the flow of data, signifying the end of a block of input data. The reading equipment and its associated circuitry must be capable of sensing the code and interpreting the data flow in the desired manner. The tape handler must bring the tape to rest without damage and without entering the next character position, or information will be lost. This requirement is rather severe when tape is being moved at 100 inches per second (the tape speed for 1000 characters per second, characters spaced ten per inch). Elaborate systems to maintain proper tape tension have been devised, all intended to preserve the primary advantage of perforated-tape equipment—the ability to stop on a stop code without coasting over into subsequent data less than $\frac{1}{10}$ inch away. In most cases, fast-acting brakes are used to halt the tape, and electronic feedback systems are employed to cause the tape reels to rotate in the necessary direction and at the necessary speed to maintain the desired tape tension.

Whatever the approach to the reading of perforated tape, we have seen that the outcome is a series of sets of 1 or 0 conditions, the coding of each set containing information in electrical form capable of being used by the computer to set its internal storage elements.

PUNCH-CARD INPUT-OUTPUT

Probably the most widely used input-output medium is the familiar punch card, which has as its two discrete states the presence or absence of material in accurately positioned locations that can be identified by a system of coordinates. Punch cards were used by the U.S. Census Bureau to process data before the turn of the century. Although the equipment with which they were used was crude, the format selected at that time led to the development of today's data-processing punch cards.

Although punch cards are relatively slow to punch and to read, they do offer numerous advantages in certain types of data-processing applications. They can be stored easily and inexpensively. They offer a moderate amount of storage, usually sufficient to hold one transaction or one name and address, or one order or sale. Punch cards have been used so extensively that a wide variety of processing machinery is available for off-line processing and on-line input and output service. Most computers have some provisions to handle punch-card information.

Most of the punch cards in existence today can be traced to equipment made by IBM or Remington Rand. Examples of these two manufacturers' cards are shown in Fig. 6–11. The main distinguishing feature is the shape of the holes;

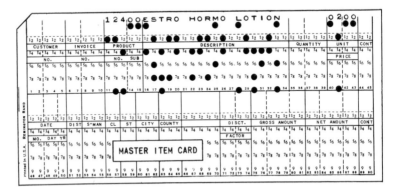

Fig. 6–11. Two types of punch cards [(a) IBM and (b) Remington Rand] commonly used in data-processing systems. Each vertical column represents one character.

IBM cards have rectangular holes and Remington Rand cards have round holes. Functionally they serve the same purpose.

PUNCH-CARD EQUIPMENT

A typical card punch is shown in Fig. 6–12. No doubt the reader has seen and handled punch cards. They are used widely by organizations that require large-scale data processing. It will be noted that the card contains a number of bit positions, similar to the computer storage register. For example, the IBM card has eighty vertical columns, each of which can store one alphanumeric character. Ten bit positions in each column are used for storing decimal numeric information. In combination with the remaining three bit positions and with appropriate codes, letters of the alphabet can also be accommodated.

Some punch-card equipment actually prints the punched information on the card, so that anyone can read the card as well as the data-processing machine. To an experienced user of punch cards, the holes have immediate meaning. Colored cards are often used to facilitate manual manipulation and sorting. So widespread is the use of punch cards that furniture manufacturers who specialize in office furniture offer several varieties of filing cabinets and drawers designed specifically for the storage of cards.

Various techniques are employed to punch and to read cards for computer purposes. Punching is achieved by passing each card over a set of punches and dies which are activated or not, depending on whether a 1 or 0 is to be stored at each bit position. Some punches, the slower variety, punch one character position or column at a time, moving typically from the left edge of the card to the right. With conventional equipment, this requires eighty starts and stops and possible punches for each card. All selected punches in each column are activated simultaneously.

Fig. 6–12. A relatively slow card punch punches one character or vertical column at a time. This unit can be operated directly by a keyboard or by any of several other character-at-a-time data sources.

A faster type of punch handles the cards crosswise, punching one horizontal row at a time, rather than a column at a time. The latter system, although considerably faster, requires more auxiliary equipment. The reason for this is as follows:

Suppose that information is being entered into a card punch by a manually operated keyboard that is capable of specifying one digit at a time. In the column-at-a-time punch, a relatively simple system can be set up to punch one column each time the keyboard is operated and to advance to the next position upon completion of each column punch. Thus the punch is *slaved* to the keyboard—when the keyboard is operated a new character is punched.

HIGH-SPEED CARD PUNCHING

In the type of punch that punches rows at a time, this one-for-one approach would be impossible. Before the first row can be punched, all eighty characters must be known and stored by the punch auxiliary equipment or the computer. Each time the punch moves the card to a new row position, it looks into the memory, and holes are punched in all positions of that row where called for by the data. This faster type of punch (see Fig. 6–13) is capable of punching 100 cards per minute when fed by a fast source of data. The slower serial type of punch takes several seconds to punch one card.

Card-punching and card-reading equipment comprise the main means of entry and exit in many high-speed electronic computers. So universal is their use that card-handling equipment is relatively inexpensive. Some equipment contains enough logical components to give the handling equipment some of the capabilities normally associated with the computer itself. Many types of conversion equipment, such as from magnetic tape and perforated tape to punch cards, are available.

By this time the reader should have learned to expect speed-up miracles from the application of electronic techniques to mechanical operations which, because of their relatively slow speed, limit performance of computing and data-

Fig. 6–13.   A high-speed card punch (100 cards per minute) requires storage of an entire card's worth of information before punching can begin. Speed is gained at the expense of cost and complexity.

processing equipment. Punch-card equipment is no exception. Several manufacturers have developed equipment for reading cards photoelectrically at rates as high as several thousand cards per minute.

MAGNETIC TAPE

Both perforated tape and punch cards suffer one severe limitation—material must be physically removed from the storage medium (which also prevents practical revision of stored information), and speed is thereby automatically limited. The "next step up" is magnetic tape, with which these limitations are removed.

Magnetic tape offers a highly efficient, extremely fast means of presenting digital information to a computer. Although magnetic recording techniques have progressed tremendously during the past decade, improvements are still being sought in many research and development laboratories.

Physically, the magnetic tape used in computer work is similar to that used in home tape recorders. The tape is usually wider and of significantly better quality, but most computer tapes have a plastic base upon which is deposited a thin film of magnetic material. The characteristics of the coating material are such that selected areas may readily be magnetized by a magnetic field. In addition, the magnetic material must be capable of retaining the magnetism until remagnetized by another magnetic field.

MAGNETIC RECORDING THEORY

Reviewing some basic principles of magnetism, we recall that similar magnetic poles tend to repel each other while dissimilar poles attract. To see how these basic phenomena make magnetic recording possible, consider the sketch shown in Fig. 6–14. The magnetic material is made up of a number of tiny pieces of magnetic material shown (greatly enlarged) as bars in the drawing. The recording device is similar to a horseshoe magnet whose ends are brought extremely close together. This particular type of horseshoe magnet is an *elec-*

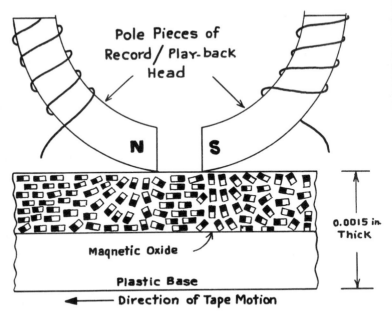

Fig. 6–14. A greatly enlarged cross section of a magnetic-recording-head gap and magnetic tape shows random alignment of magnetic particles before the tape comes under the influence of the gap. Particles leaving the gap are aligned and the resulting magnetic field is detectable. Magnetization on tape is reversed by reversing recording current in the head coil depending upon the digital data to be recorded.

tromagnet, that is, its magnetism is determined by the magnitude of electrical current flowing through a coil of wire wrapped around the midsection of the horseshoe, and the polarity is determined by the direction of current flow.

At this point, it should be pointed out that magnetic recording depends upon the motion of the tape past the recording magnet, or *head* as it is commonly called. A typical head consists of one or more magnetic elements placed very accurately in line perpendicular to the direction of the tape travel. In the diagram, the tape is assumed to be moving from right to left past the head gap, so the first bit recorded will appear on the left.

DIGITAL RECORDING ON MAGNETIC TAPE

Let us assume for a moment that the magnetic particles in the oxide coating of the tape are randomly oriented before they enter the influence of the head's magnetic field. Let us assume also that the current flowing through the head coil is in the direction shown, causing the right-hand pole piece to become a north pole and the left a south pole.

As each particle approaches the first (north) pole, the south pole of the particle is attracted toward the gap. As the particles approach the gap, they are fairly well aligned, with their south poles pointing toward the north pole of the head. In the gap, the north poles are leading their respective south poles owing to the combined influence of the head pole pieces. As the particles pass the gap, they rotate with their north poles oriented toward the south pole of the head. As tape motion continues, the particles align themselves with their north poles trailing (being attracted to the south pole whose influence they feel last), the condition they retain as they leave the influence of the head.

If the head current is reversed, the orientation of particles is reversed also. If the current reversal is abrupt, there will be a sharp line of demarcation between tape areas of different particle orientation or different polarity of magnetization.

If head current is reversed at a periodic rate, the tape pattern will consist of alternate areas of oppositely polarized particles which form a magnetic "picture" of head current. This pattern will be invisible to the human eye, but it can be read electronically.

PLAYING BACK MAGNETICALLY RECORDED DATA

To *play back* the original information, the tape is again pulled past the head gap. Here we must recall another basic principle of magnetics. A magnet has associated with it a magnetic field, which can be represented by lines spouting out of one end or pole and reentering at the other. Whenever such a magnetic field is cut by a conductor, a current is induced in that conductor.

In the magnetized areas of the tape there are many tiny magnets aligned in the same direction. The magnetic fields of each magnet combine, producing a relatively strong overall field. As this field is moved past the head gap by the motion of the tape, a current is induced in the head coil each time the magnetic tape field reverses. With suitable amplification, the original recording current can be accurately reproduced.

Thus we have stored two-state information, and we have recovered it, fulfilling the requirements for a digital storage system. Fortunately, the magnetic particles used in tape are extremely small, and thousands of bits of information can be stored in a single square inch of tape.

MAGNETIC-RECORDING FORMATS

Although magnetic tape is several times more efficient and faster than either punch cards or perforated tape, its use involves many complications. So far, we have considered only the small piece of tape adjacent to one read-write head. To be of practical use, tape equipment must be capable of handling long strips of tape, 2500 feet in length or longer.

Normally, characters are recorded on tape by recording their bits across the tape in parallel *tracks* or *channels*. Each track has associated with it a head and electronic record and playback amplifiers. The most frequently used tape systems employ seven or eight tracks, but some systems use as many as sixteen tracks. Of the several standard magnetic-tape widths, ½, ¾, and 1 inch are most common, the latter being used almost exclusively for sixteen-track work.

To study several typical methods of recording digital data on magnetic tape, refer to Fig. 6–15. Here we have six time slots numbered from 0 through 6. For each time slot a bit of digital data has been assigned. The curves below the data row show three different ways in which two-state head currents are used to record digital information.

The first curve shows the head current starting out at a low value. Upon the arrival of time slot 0, at which time it is desired to record a digital 1, a pulse of current (positive in this example) is applied to the head for a brief period of time. This 1's pulse is terminated well before the arrival of time slot 2. Because the data to be stored in time slot 2 consist of a 0, no current pulse is produced at that time, and the head current remains at its low value. At time slots 2 and 3, we want to record 1 bits, so current pulses are produced. At time slots 4 and 5, the data consist of 0's, so current through the head is inhibited. In this system, we have used one state to denote a 0 and another state to denote a 1. Because the low

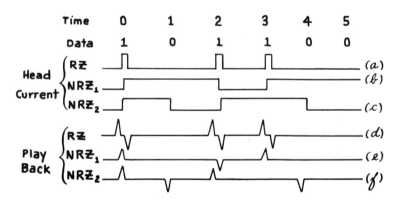

Fig. 6–15. The three most popular methods of recording digital data on magnetic tape. In (a) a pulse indicates a 1 and no pulse indicates a 0. In (b) a transition indicates a 1 and no transition indicates a 0. In (c) a transition indicates a change from whatever the previous bit was and no transition indicates that the current bit is the same as the previous one. The schemes shown in (b) and (c) are more efficient.

value used to denote 0's could be zero current, this system is referred to as the *return-to-zero* (or RZ) method of recording.

When a digital recording of the type described above is played back, a process called *differentiation* takes place, with the results shown in Fig. 6–15*d*. Notice that two pulses occur for each original bit of information, a *positive* pulse corresponding in time to the *rise* of the RZ data pulse, and a *negative* pulse coincident with the *fall* of the data pulse. In a computer that uses this recording method, the negative pulses are eliminated or clipped and circuitry is provided to examine the head output for the presence or absence of positive pulses at the appropriate time to determine the content of the stored data.

RECORDING EFFICIENCY

From our previous discussions of information-storage efficiency, it may be evident that the return-to-zero system involves waste. Why produce negative impulses that are not to be used? Can they not be eliminated? The answer is that in magnetic recording systems in which maximum efficiency is desired, they are eliminated.

Figure 6–15*b* shows one form of *non-return-to-zero* magnetic recording. In this case, a 1 bit is denoted by a *change* (in either direction) and a 0 bit is denoted by *no change*. When the NRZ$_1$ recording is played back, the signal illustrated in Fig. 6–15*e* is obtained. Note that one pulse occurs for each 1 bit. Instead of throwing away every other bit, the electronics of the system invert the negative pulses (making them positive) and mix the two resulting positive pulse signals, providing the same type of output that was obtained in the RZ case after clipping off the redundant negative pulses. Figure 6–15*c* shows another version of the NRZ recording methods in which a change indicates a change in data from either state to the other. No change, in this case, means no change in data.

NRZ VERSUS RZ RECORDING

The advantages of non-return-to-zero recording may not be immediately obvious. We previously observed that the magnetic particles were small, permitting high-density recording. There are, however, other factors that contribute to the available bit density for a given tape system. These factors affect the *number of transitions* that can safely be recorded per inch of tape. Notice that in (*a*) six transitions were needed to denote the three 1's and three 0's. In the two NRZ cases, only three transitions were necessary. Thus the NRZ system is more efficient from a data-storage density point of view.

In actual practice, the NRZ system is often used but without ever actually involving the zero current level. We have seen that digital storage is best obtained with two-state devices whose two states are as far apart as possible. So it becomes more reliable to saturate (apply maximum obtainable magnetization) the tape in one direction or the opposite direction by passing saturation current through the head in one direction or the other. In this case, NRZ recording is achieved by reversing the current for each 1 or each change, depending upon the form of NRZ recording used.

PULSE-PACKING DENSITY

Let us examine the data-storage capabilities of a typical section of magnetic tape. One of the most common tape formats is that used by most IBM data-processing machines. Seven tracks are used, and the bits (NRZ-recorded) are packed with a density of 200 per inch per track. A typical 10½-inch reel of tape, if packed solidly with information at this density, would contain more than 40 million bits of information!

Bit density (for a single track), tape speed, and bit frequency are related by the simple formula

$$f = ds$$

where f is the *frequency* in bits per second, d is the *density* in bits per inch, and s is the tape *speed* in inches per second. Because characters are normally recorded across the tape perpendicular to the direction of tape travel, the bit frequency corresponds to the character rate.

The most common tape speeds in use today fall in the range 30 to 150 inches per second. If characters are spaced 200 to the inch on tape moving at 75 inches per second, the character rate will be 15,000 characters per second. Some systems record two characters across the tape, making possible the recording of two characters at one time slot. Using this technique with a 150-inch-per-second tape speed and a bit density of 300 per inch, the effective character rate is 90,000 characters per second. Investigation now under way to increase even further the bit densities used in digital recording will result in even greater data-storage efficiency.

CLOCKING DATA ONTO TAPE

To help visualize the recording of digital information, let us consider a typical problem. We have data stored in a high-speed storage register that will produce voltage pulses defining successive characters each time a pulse is applied to terminal *(a)* (see Fig. 6–15). As in any data-processing system, there must be a source of timing, or *clock*. Here we find that with the selected tape speed we need a clock frequency of 10,000 pulses per second to record characters on the tape at a density of 100 per inch or a spacing of 0.01 inch. The tape is assumed to be moving at a constant speed, thus the clock determines the bit packing.

We use an oscillator to produce the clock and, to make sure that the same clock will be used when playing back the recorded information, we record the clock in a separate recording track. The clock track receives a 1 bit for each time slot. Similar signals, depending on the information to be stored, are emitted by the register each time a clock pulse is received. Thus 10,000 times a second the record head "sees" a simultaneous burst of pulses (or at least one pulse, the clock pulse), the combination of which defines a one character.

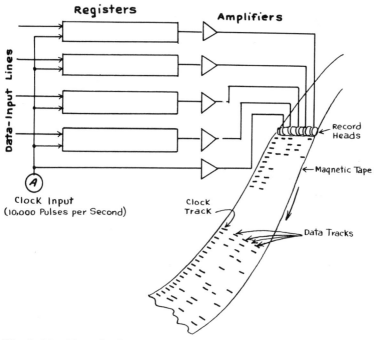

Fig. 6–16.   Digital information is clocked out of storage registers at a frequency (number of characters per second) appropriate for placing the correct number of characters per inch on the magnetic tape. A clock of 10,000 pulses per second with a tape speed of 100 inches per second will produce a *packing density* of 100 bits (characters) per inch.

The amplifier circuits shown in Fig. 6–16 accept the register pulses and produce reverse current pulses to write 1's and 0's where appropriate.

ERROR DETECTION IN MAGNETIC RECORDING

Digital magnetic recording has become such an exact technique that errors are rare in conservatively designed systems. To ensure further the faithfulness of digital magnetic recordings, several techniques are used to detect errors. One popular approach is the use of a *parity* check for each character recorded.

Assume that an imperfect tape has been used to record some digital information in binary-coded decimal form and that a small pinhole containing no oxide material passed under the headpiece assigned to the most significant bit of the character just at the time a 1 bit was to have recorded. As a result, that particular bit is dropped. This is called a *dropout*, and most tape systems are free of dropouts for millions of bits. But if a dropout occurred, the resulting number might be altogether wrong.

Parity bits offer a convenient means of assuring accurate recording by "flagging" missing or extra bits. Certain assumptions, based on statistical analysis, are made. Considering a transverse group of recorded bits across the tape, it is assumed that a good quality tape will have no more than one flaw or imperfection in any one transverse area used to record a column of bits.

PARITY CHECKING

Let us assume that we are recording six-bit binary-coded decimal characters on tape by placing the six bits for each character in as many tape tracks and clocking the characters onto the tape at a convenient rate to produce a nominal packing density.

Just before the six bits for each character are transferred to the record amplifiers, a *parity generator* quickly and automatically "counts" the number of 1 bits in that column. Using a seventh tape track for an *odd parity bit*, the parity generator causes a 1 bit to be recorded in the seventh track for each character containing an even number of 1 bits (without the parity bit). No parity bit is recorded if the character being recorded contains an odd number of 1 bits. Typical numbers and their corresponding parity bits are shown in Fig. 6–17.

While the data are being played back, another parity circuit quickly scans each character and counts the number of 1 bits. If each character (including the parity bit) contains an odd number of 1 bits, it is assumed that no bits were dropped or added. If a character is detected with an even number of 1's, it is assumed that an error has occurred.

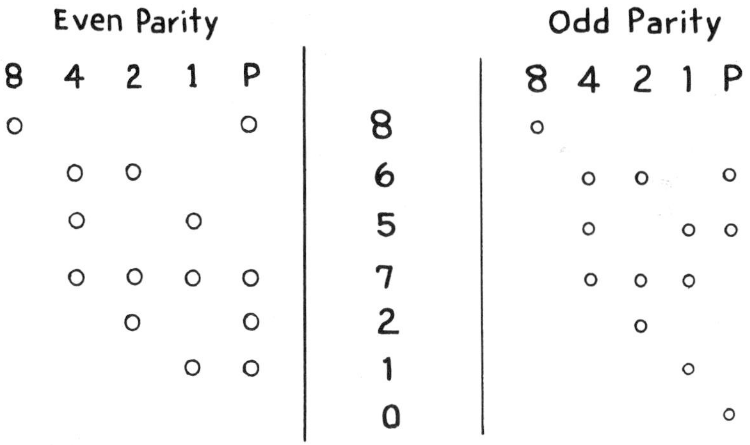

Even Parity							Odd Parity				
8	4	2	1	P			8	4	2	1	P
o				o	**8**		o				
	o	o			**6**			o	o		o
	o		o		**5**			o		o	o
	o	o	o	o	**7**			o	o	o	
		o		o	**2**				o		
			o	o	**1**					o	
					0						o

Fig. 6–17.   Parity bits are frequently used to ensure accuracy of digital data. In most cases the likelihood of simultaneous errors in a single character is remote. Thus dropping or adding one bit in any character will permit electronic checking circuits to detect errors.

Many different kinds of action may be taken upon detection of parity failures. Some programs halt the computer, some cause the data to be read again and halt the computer only if the error recurs, others send an electronic flag along with the data that are recorded with the results to warn the interpreter of the possible data error.

Some systems employ not only a *longitudinal* parity bit (across the tape), but *lateral* parity as well. In this case the 1 bits of each tape track are monitored in each track, and at regular intervals parity bits are recorded. By the combination of lateral and longitudinal parity checks, a bit dropout can be isolated and even corrected.

START-STOP TAPE HANDLERS

In a previous paragraph we saw that data could be fed into a computer at rates as high as 90,000 characters per second. At this rate, a computer's internal memory quickly becomes saturated, or full, and the input must be halted while the computer processes the information. To minimize wasted time and to optimize computer efficiency, it is imperative that the magnetic-tape machines that are used with computers be able to start and stop quickly.

Fast starting is essential because minimum time should be wasted in the presentation of new information to the computer when the computer asks for it. Both fast starts and stops are desirable to increase tape-packing efficiency; gaps must be left between blocks of data to permit stopping and starting of the tape. These can be made narrower (increasing packing efficiency) if the tape-handling machine stops and starts quickly.

Figure 6–18 shows a typical high-performance computer-type digital magnetic-tape handler. To achieve fast starts and stops, the tape is pressed against continuously running capstans by means of solenoid-operated pinch rollers.

Fig. 6–18. A typical computer-type magnetic-tape handler. Record and playback heads are on the extreme right in the center of the panel. Tension arms (upper and lower) sense tension and activate reel motors that in turn take in or put out tape to maintain tension within safe limits despite the fast starts and stops required for computer work.

Let us examine the problems that arise from this type of operation. Owing to the rapid acceleration and deceleration of the tape and the finite mass and inertia of the reels holding the tape, elaborate servo systems are used to maintain relatively constant tape tension throughout start and stop cycles. The machine illustrated in Fig. 6–19 can accommodate 3-millisecond starts and 1.5-millisecond stops at tape speeds up to 150 inches per second in either direction.

Fig. 6–19.   A high-performance magnetic-tape handler uses vacuum chambers instead of tension arms to sense tape tension. The machine shown permits starting, stopping, and reversing tape within a few milliseconds at tape speeds of up to 150 inches per second.

Tape is often used as an intermediate output device in digital computer systems. Because of its high-speed capabilities, minimum computer time is wasted in turning out results if tape is used as an output device. Unfortunately, tape is virtually impossible to interpret by human beings, so it can serve only as an intermediate storage for another output device capable of producing results in a form suitable for human interpretation. But the latter operation can be achieved off-line, freeing the computer for other problems.

HIGH-SPEED PRINTING

One of the most common forms of output device is the high-speed digital printer. The most sophisticated form of computer output printer is the line-at-a-time printer. With suitable input (output from the computer or from an intermediate magnetic-tape handler) the printers can print the equivalent of one page in this book in less than 2 seconds!

In printer systems of this type, one line's worth of data is shifted into the printer memory at the beginning of each print cycle. Standard printers are available from several manufacturers for printing lines of up to 120 characters at line rates as high as twenty per second!

In an on-line application, the printer receives its input directly from the computer. In this case, depending on individual speed capabilities, either the computer or the printer may limit the speed of output. Normally the computer is much faster than the printer, dictating the use of magnetic tape as intermediate storage. In these cases, the computer transfers its output information onto the magnetic tape, usually in block form with just one line's worth per block. No computer time is wasted in making such a transfer of data.

The tape thus recorded is played into the printer memory in bursts. Each time the printer completes a print cycle it "requests" more data from the magnetic tape. The tape handler starts the tape, reads in another block, and stops. The printer completes that line and calls for more data.

LINE-AT-A-TIME PRINTERS

In preceding discussions we have seen how alphanumeric characters can be defined by six bits of information. Advantage is taken of this situation in the high-speed printers. The printer memory (for 120 columns) must be capable of storing 6 × 120, or 720, bits of information. This transfer may be achieved in several ways, two of which are illustrated in Fig. 6–20. The most common case involves the transfer of characters in serial or sequential fashion. Each character is comprised of four or six bits of information conveyed on as

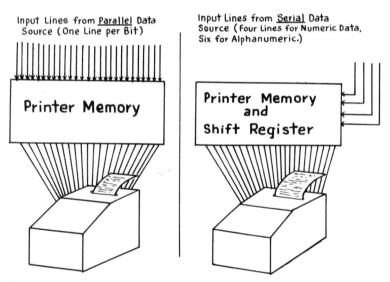

Fig. 6–20.   High-speed line-at-a-time printers must contain one line's worth of storage. Such storage systems can be fed in parallel (all data simultaneously) or serially, depending upon speed requirements and applications. Serial feed requires fewer connections between the source and the printer but more complication in the printer storage system.

many wires from the source to the printer. In this mode, 120 steps are required. If the data-transfer rate is 10,000 per second, each step will require 100 microseconds and 0.012 second will be required for the complete transfer. To this must be added any time required to accelerate the tape mechanism or to otherwise activate the data source. The other case involves the simultaneous transfer of all bits from the source to the printer, or from a secondary buffer that accumulates the data sequentially and makes a parallel transfer to the printer memory.

The basic mechanism of a line-at-a-time printer is a drum (see Fig. 6–21). This contains as many sets of type as there are columns to be printed and is rotated continuously at a convenient speed, typically 900 rpm. Each set of type has associated with it a fast-acting solenoid-operated hammer which is positioned radially with respect to the drum.

Attached to the drum shaft is a set of code wheels. Detectors sensing the changing code combinations produced by these code wheels produce electrical codes that correspond to the character that appears opposite each hammer at any given instant. Through the use of 120 digital comparator circuits (which can physically be the same elements as those used to store data in the printer's memory system), the hammer-striking time for each column can be accurately determined. So the hammers remain still until the appropriate character appears, whereupon they are activated by electronic circuits to cause the desired impression to be made on the paper. When the drum has completed one revolution, all possible characters will have been made available to all character positions and the line will be printed.

During the above operation, the paper has been at rest. Upon completion of the print cycle, two things happen. The paper-feed mechanism is activated, and the data source is notified that new information may be loaded into the printer memory. Because paper feeding is a mechanical process, the

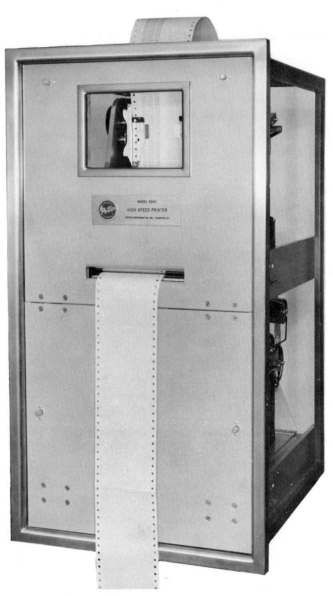

Fig. 6–21. High-speed line-at-a-time printers of the type shown are capable of printing up to twenty lines per second of numeric information or ten lines per second of alphanumeric information. Data can be fed directly from the computer or via an intermediate storage medium such as magnetic tape.

paper-feed time usually exceeds the memory-loading time. When both are completed, another print cycle is initiated.

PRINTING FORMATS

There are many complications that can occur in the generation of printed material from such a digital system. In most cases, data must be printed in preselected positions on the paper. It is often necessary to skip lines, in which case only the paper-feed mechanism is activated. In some cases identical data must be printed at more than one location on the paper. Instructions for such "formatting" can be contained either along with the input data, or in an auxiliary storage or format data source, depending upon the type of equipment used and the application.

Parallel-printing equipment of the type just described is typical of most modern high-speed data-processing systems (see Fig. 6–22). Several more sophisticated (and much more

Fig. 6–22.   Where the quantity of information to be processed is great, off-line data-processing equipment is often used. The special-purpose system shown accepts magnetic-tape information and produces printed copy at rates up to fifteen lines per second with 120 characters per line. (*Courtesy Potter Instrument Co.*)

costly) systems are under development. Some eliminate the mechanical processes by substituting combinations of electronic and photographic techniques. Some form characters by systems of styluses arranged in matrices that print by means of small, closely spaced dots in appropriate positions for each particular character or symbol to be printed.

PLOTTERS AS OUTPUT DEVICES

In some types of digital computer applications, it is desired that the output be in the form of curves. These can be

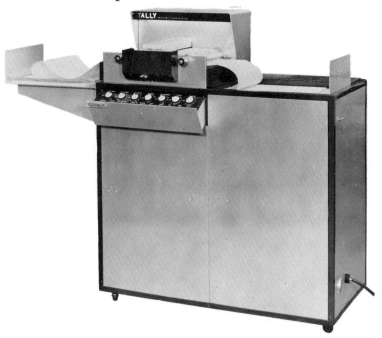

Fig. 6–23.   Digital plotters are frequently used as computer output devices, particularly where results are desired in the form of a "picture" showing relationships between different parameters. The Model 201 digital plotter plots up to twenty "points" per second when fed information from a suitable digital source. Points form curves giving a graphic plot. *(Courtesy Tally Register Corp.)*

obtained in a number of ways. For example, the digital output of the computer can be applied to a digital-to-analog converter, producing analog signals that can be recorded on a conventional pen-type or oscillographic recorder.

Another approach to the plotting of digital-system output is the *digital plotter* shown in Fig. 6–23. The digital input required for this device consists of seven binary-coded decimal characters for each point. Three of these tell how far to the left or right the next point will be, another three tell how high the new point will be, and the remaining character specifies the type of symbol to be used to identify a particular plot. This plotter can print up to four different symbols at rates as high as twenty points per second when fed digital information from a suitable source.

· 7 ·

HOW COMPUTERS REMEMBER

The ability of a digital computer to "remember" can be an important factor in determining its usefulness. Particularly in data-processing applications, a computer's memory capacity is almost directly proportional to its operating efficiency. Also of major importance is the speed with which information can be placed in and withdrawn from the various memory systems in the machine.

As indicated above, computer memory systems can be rated according to speed and size. Because these two important characteristics are incompatible, most computers employ combinations of high-speed limited-capacity memories and low-speed large-capacity memories. In both cases ratings are relative, because slow speed to a digital computer can be quite fast in comparison with other types of equipment.

TYPES OF MEMORIES

Computers can store information in such devices as magnetic cores, magnetic drums, perforated and magnetic tapes, discs, and many others. Choice of appropriate storage devices is usually made by the manufacturer from a study of the applications for which his machine is intended. Because computers are not always used exclusively for one type of computation, most manufacturers offer several forms of memories as optional features of their systems.

Most computers have at least a limited amount of fast-access storage, which is used where speed is important. That is, registers contained in this portion of the system's memory can be reached quickly and directly when they are required by the program and are, therefore, usually used for temporary storage of information.

The fast-access part of the computer's memory is usually comprised of magnetic cores or portions of a drum storage specially designed to give fast access for storage and withdrawal of information. Cores, in general, provide faster access but are expensive, particularly for large-capacity memories. Drums have a maximum access time that is somewhat greater than that of cores, but for large-capacity storage systems, the drum has a cost advantage. Some of the smaller computers employ only drum storage, trading speed limitations for economy. Some have combinations of drums and cores with provisions for transferring information back and forth to take maximum advantage of both types of storage.

Another part of the memory of most computers is the slow-access storage, which is usually capable of storing considerable quantities of information. This storage can be in the form of tape or large drums without provisions for high-speed access. This part of the memory is used to store information where extremely fast access is not required or where relatively slow access can be tolerated. Some systems are arranged in such a way that information can be withdrawn from storage while other processes are in progress, thus eliminating the delays imposed by the relative slowness of the storage device.

Because a computer manufacturer never really knows how much storage will be required for a given application, he usually makes provisions for the addition of many storage systems so that the customer can expand his storage capacity by adding drums or tape units.

MEMORY-ACCESS TIMES

In magnetic-core memories, information is stored in tiny magnetic elements, each of which is connected to input-output circuits that can *address* any selected portion of the memory. On magnetic drums, data are stored on the drum surface. The drum rotates continuously, bringing every portion of the stored information to the read-write heads once for each turn of the drum. In tape systems, information is stored on long strips of tape, and the tape is moved past read-write heads to gain access to any selected portion of the stored information.

If a computer uses a multiplicity of tape units for medium-speed information storage, each tape unit is assigned a number so that the computer can call for one or the other as the need arises.

Each computer storage device has a unique address that is known to the computer programmer and to which access is possible from the input-output equipment and the various working registers of the computer. As he becomes familiar with his machine, the programmer first learns the characteristics of the various storage locations and, in writing his program, uses them to best advantage whenever possible.

Mention has been made of storage elements comprised of active elements, such as tubes and transistors. In that discussion, two basic requirements for such storage devices were given: (1) that they must be capable of being *set* (that is, remotely adjusted to one stable state or another), and (2) that they must be capable of being interrogated remotely.

Storage devices made up of active elements can be extremely fast and convenient to use. With proper circuitry, an almost perfect storage device can be fabricated, but the cost is usually high. As a result, this type of storage device is usually reserved for use in locations where high speed is important, for example, in an input-output register where access to and from the storage may occur many thousands of times during the processing of data for a single problem. Here any delays would be multiplied by the number of times access is required.

Memory systems that are made up of active elements are usually of small capacity because of their cost. In the larger systems, cores and drums are most commonly used.

MAGNETIC-CORE PROPERTIES

In the magnetic-core memory system, tiny magnetic elements shaped like doughnuts and half the size of the letter o's on this page are used as storage elements. These doughnuts, or *toroids*, are made of a material called *ferrite*. Their manufacture is carefully controlled to ensure uniform electrical and mechanical characteristics. Even after this careful manufacturing process, each core (and there may be hundreds of thousands in a large computer memory system) is individually tested and spare cores are provided, in case they may be needed.

The materials that are used to make memory cores exhibit magnetic properties that cause them to be uniquely adaptable for two-state memory use. Technically speaking, they exhibit rectangular-hysteresis-loop characteristics. Let us briefly examine basic magnetic theory and see how this property gives these elements their memory capability.

A new piece of rectangular-hysteresis-loop material (commonly referred to as *square-loop* material) exhibits no detectable magnetic properties of its own. If, however, the material is subjected to a magnetic field, its particles align themselves with the field. Owing to a property of square-loop material known as *retentivity*, the aligned particles retain their orderly alignment when the external magnetic field is removed. Low-retentivity materials (such as soft iron) lose their magnetization when the field is removed. It is the high-retentivity materials that are useful as two-state memory devices.

An additional desirable property for memory-core materials is that the change from one state (particles aligned in one direction) to the opposite state (particles aligned in the opposite direction) must be abrupt. That is, if the material is subjected momentarily to a magnetic field, it will retain a large percentage of the magnetism imparted by that field. If the same core is slowly subjected to a field of the opposite polarity, the original magnetization will be retained until the new field "takes over" and the particles realign themselves abruptly with the new field. Ideally the change should take place instantaneously.

MAGNETIC-CORE CIRCUITS

Figure 7–1 shows a typical core, greatly enlarged, with a wire passing through its center. When an electric current is passed through the wire, a magnetic field is set up around the wire. If the current is strong enough, the field will be sufficient to magnetize the core surrounding the wire.

If we imagine the current passing through the wire as starting at zero and increasing gradually in one direction, the core will become progressively more and more magnetized until a point called *saturation magnetization* is reached. At this point, almost all the core particles are aligned along the axis of the magnetic field produced by the current-carrying wire. Further increase in current will have little additional effect on the core's magnetization. With an ideal high-retentivity material, the same magnetic condition will remain when the current is removed. Furthermore, the same condi-

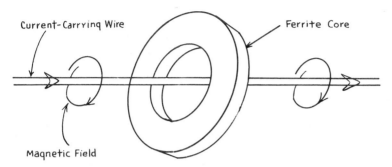

Current-Carrying Wire

Ferrite Core

Magnetic Field

Fig. 7–1. Magnetic cores, half the size of the letter o's on this page, are widely used in computer memory systems where fast access is required. Current-carrying wire magnetizes the core. The core retains magnetization even after the current is removed, storing one bit of information.

tion will continue to exist as the current is slowly increased in the opposite direction (causing the external magnetic field to reverse polarity). The retentivity of the material is such that the particles retain their magnetized orientation even though the external field opposes them.

If we continue to increase the opposing current, a point will be reached at which the external field becomes predominant. Abruptly the magnetic particles realign themselves with the new field.

From this brief study of an ideal material (which can be closely approached in practice), we can think of a core as having its particles aligned in one direction or the opposite direction. Thus we have a two-state device if currents are of sufficient magnitude to cause saturation. One state exists after a positive current pulse is applied to the wire, and the opposite state exists after a negative current pulse is applied. Arbitrarily, let us assign a logic 1 to the state that results from a positive pulse and a logic 0 to the opposite state that results from a negative current pulse.

To change the state of a saturated core we must pass through the wire a current of sufficient magnitude to switch the core to the opposite direction. Owing to the high retentivity of the core material, the core will retain stored information indefinitely, or until the information is removed by passing a reverse current through the wire.

Previously, we established a second requirement for a useful storage device: We must be able to interrogate the device or to read out the information stored in it. Fortunately, there is a convenient method for doing this with magnetic cores.

SENSING CORE CONDITIONS

Let us pass another wire through the core, as illustrated in Fig. 7–2. If we connect a sensitive meter to this wire, a signal will appear on the wire *each time the core is switched.* If a bit has been stored in the core and we want to determine whether it was a 1 or 0 (whether it has been set by the input data or left in its 0 state), we pass a negative current pulse

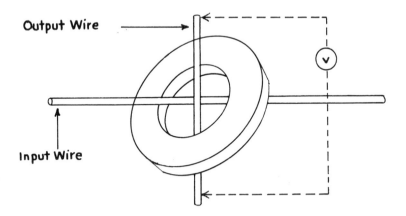

Fig. 7–2.   By applying reverse current pulse to input wire (or separate wire provided for that purpose), the core will be reset if a 1 has been stored. Reset causes a detectable signal to be induced in an output sense wire. This is the technique used to interrogate memory cores.

through the input wire. If this pulse causes the core to switch, an output signal will be detected, signifying that the core *had* previously been set (by a positive pulse) and thus contained a 1 bit. If upon interrogation by a negative pulse no output signal is detected, it can be assumed that the core did not switch (it was already in its 0 state), indicating that it was not set by the input data and thus contained a 0.

Two features should be stressed at this time. The magnetic core has *permanent* memory in the sense that once set it will remain set indefinitely until reset. No additional power is required to preserve its state. However, the only practical way to interrogate a core is to reset it. Thus the information is lost during the readout process. This is called *destructive readout,* because the data are destroyed during the process.

In many cases, destructive readout presents no problem, in fact, it is often a useful feature. But in some applications it is necessary to interrogate a memory system repeatedly without destroying the stored data in the process. Methods have been devised for reinstating the data after each interrogation. These use the logical output obtained during interrogation to activate selective setting circuits that set 1's where necessary to reestablish the stored information.

MULTIPLE-CORE SYSTEMS

A single core is obviously of little value in storing digital information. We have learned that at least four bits of storage are required to remember one binary-coded decimal numeric digit. Figure 7–3 shows how four cores can be arranged to store four bits of information. If the "load" switch is momentarily closed and the toggle switches are set in accordance with the input information, all 1's cores will be set by the resulting positive current pulse. If we now momentarily close the "read" switch, a negative current pulse will result. Those cores that were set by the "load" pulse will be switched to

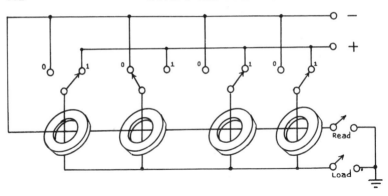

Fig. 7–3. A simple circuit shows the use of toggle switches to load and read four magnetic cores. Using the binary code, four such cores can store four possible conditions. Use of mechanical switches would be impractical because of their limited speed compared with the properties of cores.

their 0 state, or reset, and their respective sense wires will produce detectable output signals. No output signals will appear on the cores containing 0's because they do not switch.

ELECTRONIC SWITCHING

In the foregoing examples, we have used toggle switches for simplicity and ease of explanation. Mechanical switches of this type are obviously unsuited to high-speed switching of the kind required for computer memory systems. They are too slow, and they must be set manually. In all memory systems that employ magnetic cores as the storage elements, electronic current switches are used. Each of the mechanical switches illustrated previously could be replaced by an electronic equivalent, but more-efficient methods of switching, which take maximum advantage of both the electronic switches and the magnetic elements, have been devised.

The current required to switch even the tiniest magnetic core with a single wire field is quite substantial in terms of electronic switching. Because the magnetizing currents must be switched by tubes or transistors or other magnetic devices, this creates a problem.

Figure 7–4 shows a system that offers several advantages, one of which is the fact that each electronic switch must carry only about half the total magnetizing current. In addition, it provides a convenient means of addressing selected portions of the storage system.

HALF-CURRENT ADDRESSING

In this circuit, each switch introduces a current equal to half the value required for saturation magnetization of a core. If positive *half currents* are simultaneously passed through two intersecting wires, the core at the intersection will experience two half currents, or effectively one full current, and it will be set. All other cores linked by either wire will be virtually unaffected because half currents, by themselves,

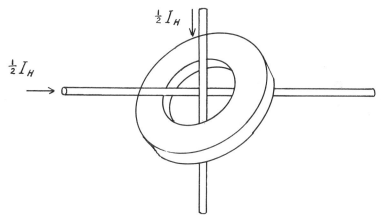

Fig. 7–4. Electronic core selection is achieved by passing half currents through cores simultaneously. Only cores at the intersection of adding half currents will be set. Similar techniques are used for selective resetting for readout.

have relatively little effect on the core material. In readout of the memory, only the core at the intersection of two negative or resetting half currents will be reset.

Computer designers use this technique to distribute digital data throughout a memory system. The first digit is stored in the first storage location by activating the input switches in accordance with the data to be stored and the line linking the first set of cores. Changing the input data and pulsing the second set of cores causes the second digit to be stored in the appropriate location, and so on.

CORE-PLANE CONSTRUCTION

In practice, cores are mounted on planes, as shown in Fig. 7–5. Cores are seldom used except where the storage capacity exceeds several hundred or thousand bits. In the manufacture of planes, the cores are carefully aligned in special jigs and hair-thin wires are passed through them with long, thin needles made of hypodermic-needle material. Wire ends are then soldered to their frames and the core planes are assembled in multiple-layer systems for memory use.

Core planes in this configuration form three-dimensional systems that require an additional piece of address information. In addition to selecting the proper core in a plane, the proper plane must be specified.

One method of obtaining this type of selection is to pass the information-containing half currents through all cores of the system. Half currents of similar polarity are passed through the selected word positions of all planes, but opposing currents (or *inhibit* currents) are passed through unselected cores. The cores that receive the latter are not activated because two positive half currents and one negative half current have the net effect of one positive half current, which is insufficient to set the unselected cores.

Fig. 7–5. Typical computer memory core planes that are capable of storing up to several thousand bits of information. (*Courtesy General Ceramics.*)

CORE-MEMORY LOGIC

In a practical system of this kind, electronic counters may be used to "keep track" of the various storage locations. Counters are particularly useful in cases where data are inserted in the exact sequence in which they will be removed from the memory. This type of operation is called *serial-in/*

serial-out. In such cases, the counters control circuits that pass half currents through each set of cores in sequence. Where a memory system will be completely filled before it is emptied, a single counter can be used for load and readout operations. Where readout may be required before loading is complete, separate counters must be used.

In most core-memory applications, however, random access is desirable. That is, the computer must be able to address any desired storage location for loading or reading out information. In this case, decoding *matrices* are used to translate the computer's address command into a current pulse on the selected wire to load or read out a particular data location.

In this type of system, data may be entered in serial fashion and read out in random fashion, or vice versa, depending on the application and the computer program.

Most computer memory systems are tailor-made to meet the specific requirements of the machine. But certain types of core memory systems are frequently called for; as a result, several manufacturers have designed standard packages to do a certain job. These are often spoken of as having certain "lengths" and "widths" (or "depths"), and they are usually made up of three-dimensional core arrangements with appropriate circuitry for flexible addressing by the computer. Word length refers to the number of bits that can be inserted in parallel (simultaneously) and depth refers to the number of such groups or words that the memory can hold.

TYPICAL CORE-MEMORY SYSTEMS

Figure 7–6 shows a commercially packaged memory system capable of storing 144 eight-bit characters or words. This unit occupies only 5½ inches of computer rack space and contains all the necessary electronic counters and amplifiers to sequence data loading and readout. This particular unit

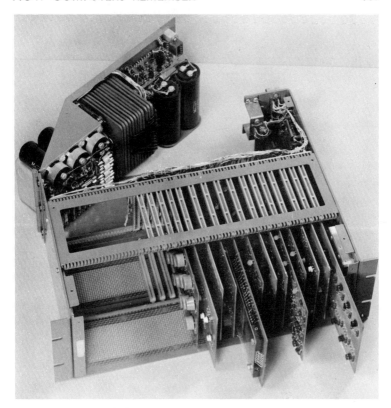

Fig. 7–6. A typical commercial package using coincident-current magnetic cores to store 144 characters of eight bits each. Character input and output rates as high as 100,000 per second are possible. The complete memory system occupies less than a cubic foot. (*Courtesy General Ceramics.*)

can load or read out information at rates as high as 100,000 characters per second. Figure 7–7 illustrates the logic of this memory system.

In a memory system of this kind, considerable circuitry is required to sequence the various operations required for either a load or readout cycle. Most computers have a basic *clock* that produces action pulses at regular intervals. It is

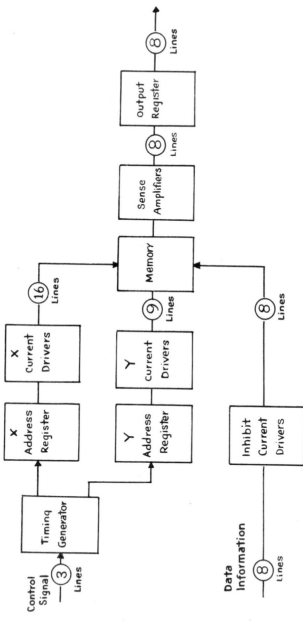

Fig. 7-7. A block diagram of the memory system illustrated in Fig. 7-6. Logic voltage levels are applied in proper sequence at the data-information input terminals. Upon application of a "load" control signal (which may be applied almost simultaneously), the corresponding code will be stored in the next available character position of the memory. Application of a "read" pulse causes the next stored character to be read out and applied to the output lines in the form of voltage levels.

usually desirable for the memory system to accept or produce information at a rate of one character or one word for each clock pulse. To do this, the various load and readout operations required for each cycle of operation must be timed internally in the memory system. This may be achieved by an internal timing system, indicated by the *timing generator* in Fig. 7–7.

The memory system illustrated has eight data-input terminals plus input terminals for such commands as load, readout, clear, and reset. Upon a load command the conditions applied to the data-input terminals (in the form of voltage levels) are transferred to the first available storage location. Immediately the load counter is advanced by one count, conditioning the load circuits to route the next input word to the next storage position.

CORE MEMORIES AS BUFFERS

Use of magnetic-core memory systems as *buffers* is quite common. In such cases, the serial-in/serial-out type of system, with the addressing controlled by counters, is ideal. Because all computers have limited high-speed storage (such as a random-access core memory), input data must be inserted in batches. In such cases, data is often inserted from magnetic tape. But the computer's main memory system is usually operated in synchronism with the computer's clock, and it is extremely difficult to synchronize a magnetic-tape mechanism to produce characters at this precise rate. Furthermore, it is often desirable to activate the input device while the main memory of the computer is in use. Thus a buffer must be provided. Data is *clocked* into the buffer at a rate determined by the input device and subsequently into the computer memory, using the computer's clocks for synchronizing.

Thus we see that the coincident-current core represents a powerful tool in the hands of the computer designer. The simplicity of the basic storage element, the core, is somewhat misleading as far as the over-all system is concerned. From the foregoing discussion of core systems, it will be recognized that considerable circuitry is required to make use of cores as storage elements. So extensive is this circuitry that coincident-current cores are seldom used in small computers, and their cost adds considerably to the larger machines. Certain electrical and mechanical requirements must be met regardless of the number of cores involved, and the cost of these cannot be amortized effectively over a few cores.

MAGNETIC SHIFT REGISTERS

There are other magnetic elements that, although more expensive individually, require less circuitry to operate and are thus more economical for small memory applications. These are normally called *shift-register* elements, and memory systems employing them are called *shift registers* (see Fig. 7–8).

The magnetic shift register is similar in function to the serial-in/serial-out coincident-current core buffer. Shift registers can be made to operate somewhat faster than coincident-current cores. Figure 7–8b shows a simplified diagram of a two-bit shift register. Data are always applied to the first location in serial fashion. Initially, the first character is stored in the first location. When the second character arrives at the input, a shift pulse is applied to the shift input and the first character is transferred to the second storage location, leaving the first location free to accept the second character to be stored. This process continues until the first character appears in the last storage location of the register.

The register is then full. Further application of shift pulses will cause the data to appear in sequential fashion at the output.

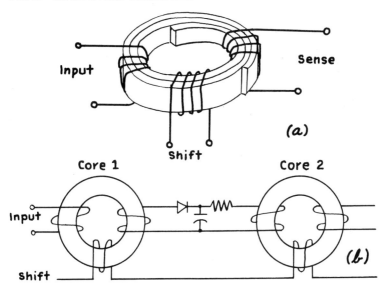

Fig. 7–8. Shift-register elements are somewhat more expensive to manufacture, but for small memory and buffer systems they offer the advantage of requiring less associated circuitry. Shift-register cores are comprised of thin strips of magnetic material wound to form a small doughnut, or toroid, around which coils are wound.

SHIFT-REGISTER ELEMENTS

The basic shift-register element is shaped like a doughnut. The core is built up by winding thin strips of magnetic material on a nonmagnetic bobbin to form the doughnut or toroid. The material used has somewhat different properties than the material used in coincident-current memories, but both must have square-loop characteristics.

Instead of single wires passing through the elements, coils of wire are wound around shift-register elements and the ends of the coils are connected to form a chain of elements.

Shift-register manufacturers have somewhat more control over the speed and current requirements of this type of element because they can vary the type of material used, the amount of material, and the number of turns contained on the coils.

The basic shift-register device is more expensive than the coincident-current core because each device contains two elements, the main or permanent storage and a temporary storage element, which eliminates the need for some of the external logic required for the coincident-current system. The magnetic core serves as the main storage device, and a capacitor performs the temporary storage.

OPERATION OF SHIFT REGISTERS

The basic shift-register device contains three windings, each containing many turns of wire. The *input* winding (see Fig. 7–9) receives a current pulse if a 1 bit is to be stored in the element and no current pulse if a 0 is to be stored. Since

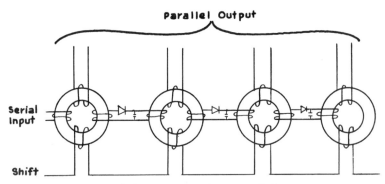

Fig. 7–9. Typical shift-register application of the *quarter turn* or serial-to-parallel shift register. Data appear one bit at a time. When four bits have been shifted in, another shift pulse is applied and the parallel outputs monitored. Pulses will occur at outputs associated with cores that have been set to store 1's.

the shift-register core has high retentivity, the new state will be retained even after the current pulse is removed.

The *shift* winding furnishes power during the shifting process. This power originates in a master *driver* circuit that passes shift pulses through all shift-winding coils of the shift register. The *sense* winding is used to read the information out of the core for transfer to the next core in the line.

Let us assume that a series of pulses is applied to the one-bit-wide shift register pictured in Fig. 7–9. The effect of such a series of pulses should be to store a series of 1's in the shift-register memory system.

Upon the arrival of the first pulse, which is applied to the input winding of the first core, that core will be magnetized, or *set*. The core retains this condition after the input pulse has expired. A pulse of opposite magnetizing effect applied to the shift winding of all cores will cause all cores that have been set to *reset*. Because the first core was set by the first input pulse, it will reset, and, in switching, a current pulse will be induced in the sense winding of that core. (If the core had not been set, the shift pulse would have a negligible effect on the core, and no output would appear on the sense winding.)

SHIFT-REGISTER CIRCUITS

It will be noticed that an *input* pulse will also induce an output pulse in the sense winding, but it will be of opposite polarity to the pulses caused by the shift pulses. The diode shown in Fig. 7–9 acts as an insulator to pulses of this undesired polarity, barring them from the following circuit.

The diode serves another useful purpose. In the shift-register circuit, the capacitor is allowed to *charge* when the shift pulse causes its associated core to switch from a 1 state to a 0. The diode, being a unidirectional device, prevents discharge of the capacitor back into the current source with the result that the capacitor discharges through the input winding of the succeeding stage, causing the 1 to be transferred some time after the shift pulse has occurred. It is this delay that makes it possible for all shift-register elements to be reset by the shift pulse and appropriate cores to be reset after the shift pulse disappears.

Thus information entered into the input of a shift register is always shifted step by step toward the output. Shift registers are used often to serialize parallel data and vice versa. As a typical example, consider a data source in which bits are being produced in sequential fashion in descending order of significance. To illustrate, assume that the binary number for 9, or 1001, is applied to a register in serial fashion.

The first bit to arrive is a 1, referring to 2^3, the next a 0 for 2^2, then another 0 for 2^1, and finally another 1 for 2^0. Let us assume that it is desired to insert these four bits in parallel (simultaneously) into another storage location.

MULTIPLE-BIT SHIFT REGISTERS

Using a four-bit shift register whose elements contain an additional winding, as shown in Fig. 7–9, the four bits are applied in sequence in the manner described above. Upon receipt of the fourth bit, the new sense windings are activated (electronically) and an additional shift pulse is applied to the system. All four cores will be reset to 0. Those that were set to 1 by the serial input data will produce simultaneous output pulses on their respective sense windings. Those that were storing 0's will produce no output signals. It should be noticed that the readout shift pulse will also cause the data to be shifted serially, but this usually presents no problem. The old information simply "spills over" the end of the register and disappears.

Similar techniques are employed to serialize parallel data. In this case parallel inputs are applied (simultaneously) to additional input windings. The bits thus stored can be shifted to the serial output in normal fashion.

This type of "corner turning" is frequently encountered in digital computers. Additional examples will be mentioned in connection with the more detailed discussions of computer operations to follow.

OTHER TYPES OF SHIFT REGISTERS

Shift registers take on several forms other than the magnetic core. Some employ vacuum tubes and transistors. Another magnetic-core type employs two cores per bit of storage, eliminating the need for the capacitor and diode. In all cases, the shift register is characterized by serial operation. The information is shifted one step at a time, upon command, and the input-core's state is dictated each time by the input data. The state of each succeeding core is determined by the state of the core preceding it at the time the shift pulse is applied.

The shift register is also a destructive type of memory, that is, on being shifted to the output, the data are destroyed. In some cases this is undesirable. To preserve stored data, the final, or output, location can be connected back to the input with appropriate switching. As data are shifted out of the last stage, they are reinserted at the input, provided no new information is being entered. External counting and timing circuitry are used to keep track of the position of the data within the system in this kind of "tail-chasing" shift-register memory operation.

ACOUSTIC MEMORIES

A type of storage system that employs the same principle as the tail-chasing shift register is the acoustic memory. Although subject to many limitations, and not too popular among modern computer manufacturers, this type of storage offers some advantages for certain types of applications.

The acoustic memory takes advantage of the fact that sound waves travel through certain materials at a constant rate. In Fig. 7–10 a pickup, which can be likened to a microphone, is placed in contact with one end of a piece of material and a transducer, similar to an earphone or loudspeaker, is connected to the other end. If serial digital information in the form of pulses of sound or no pulses of sound is applied to the transducer at a constant rate, the resultant sound waves will travel through the material and will be picked up by the microphone. With proper timing circuits and ampli-

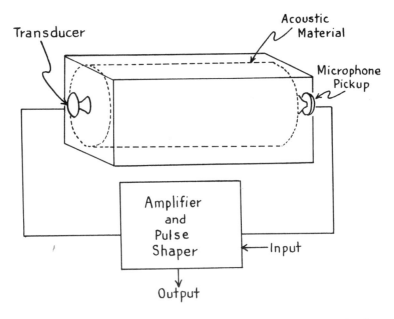

Fig. 7–10. Acoustic memories have many interesting properties, but in case of power failure, all stored data are lost. Information is stored serially in a circulating loop with bits taking the form of sound-wave pulses traveling through acoustic material. Precise timing equipment is required for this type of memory.

fiers, digital data can be recirculated indefinitely by feeding the amplified pulses of sound energy picked up by the microphone back into the transducer. With a synchronized interrogation system, the presence or absence of 1's and 0's in selected bit locations can be determined and data can be changed at will.

The acoustic memory has little value in systems that require parallel access to stored data, unless serial-to-parallel and parallel-to-serial registers (corner turners) are employed. One of the main disadvantages of the acoustic memory is the fact that if a momentary power failure should occur, all information is lost because data must constantly be recirculated for the system to be effective.

MAGNETIC-DRUM MEMORIES

One of the earliest and still most useful types of digital storage is the magnetic drum. The drum provides the most-economical means of storing large quantities of data and furnishing reasonably fast access for data entry and readout. Once recorded on a drum, data will remain stored until *erased*, and drum-stored information can be read out indefinitely without disturbing the stored data.

The drum, cylindrical in shape, is rotated at a constant speed by an electric motor. The outer surface of the drum is coated or plated with a magnetic material.

Mounted around the drum at regular axial intervals (usually spaced twenty or more per inch) may be as many as 500 record-playback heads, each accommodating one recording track. At least one head is devoted to a *clock track*. The clock track contains all 1's. The playback amplifier associated with the clock track produces a constant train of accurately timed pulses that identify accurately spaced data-storage locations around the periphery of the drum (see Figs. 7–11 and 7–12).

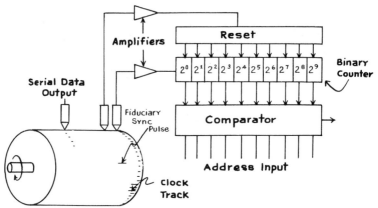

Fig. 7–11.   Magnetic drums provide the most economical medium for storing large quantities of data with reasonably fast access time. Bits are recorded as magnetic spots or transitions in multiple tracks around the periphery of the cylindrical drum surface. Electronic counters, activated by pulses derived from a special clock track, keep track of data storage positions.

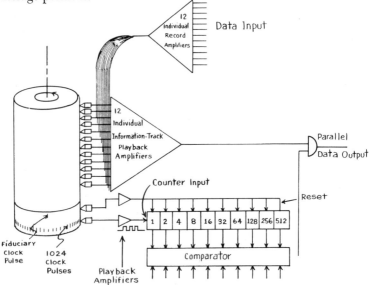

Fig. 7–12.   In some cases it is desirable to record data in parallel on multiple tracks of a drum. The fiduciary clock track, containing just one pulse, helps to identify the beginning of the data-locating-and-timing clock track.

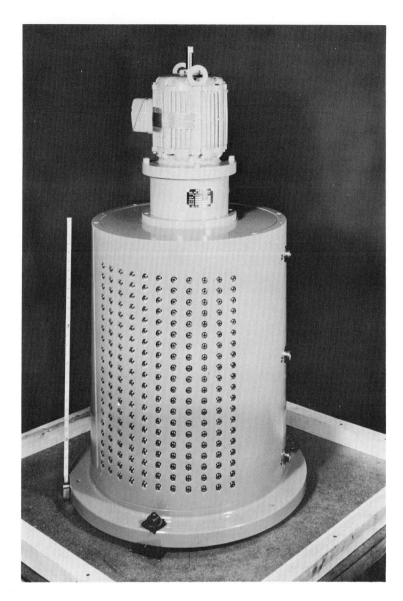

Fig. 7–13. A typical computer storage drum has provisions for mounting hundreds of record-playback heads and storing millions of bits of digital information. The tape measure at the left is extended to 30 inches.

Drum record-playback heads are identical in principle to magnetic-tape heads, except that they are spaced a small distance from the recording surface, usually 0.001 inch (see Figs. 7–13, 7–14, and 7–15). With this spacing, pulse densities as high as 200 bits per inch of circumference are attainable. Some experimental drums are operated at much higher packing densities.

The rotational speed of the drum and the number of bits around its periphery determine the clock frequency. The diameter of the drum, the packing density, and the number of tracks determine the amount of data that a drum can store (see Fig. 7–16).

DRUM-RECORDING TECHNIQUES

A typical drum 5 inches in diameter and 12 inches in length can thus store 625,000 bits of information. If rotated at a speed of 3600 revolutions per minute, the time required for the drum to make one complete revolution will be approximately 0.017 second, which is the maximum time required to reach any selected portion of the drum storage. Switching between heads can be achieved electronically or electromechanically, depending upon the speed requirements of the system.

As an example of a typical drum memory system, consider a drum that has a clock track that contains 1024 permanently recorded bits. Usually the clock track will be accurately *closed* upon itself, so the last pulse and the first pulse are spaced exactly the same amount as all other pulses in the clock track.

The constant output from the clock-track head is amplified and applied to a binary electronic counter whose ten stages are arranged so that the input pulses alternately turn the first stage *on* and *off*, and each succeeding stage has its condition changed each time the stage preceding it goes off.

Fig. 7–14. A magnetic storage drum featuring open construction shows an actual recording surface in the center. This model (5 inches in diameter and 12 inches long) is capable of storing 625,000 bits of information in as many as 240 tracks. (*Courtesy Bryant Computer Products.*)

Thus connected, the ten-stage counter assumes a unique combination of on and off stages for each clock-pulse position around the drum. To *address* a particular data-storage location, the computer produces a code corresponding to the desired location; when this code and the contents of the clock-track counter are identical, the selected location has been obtained.

Fig. 7–15. This close-up shows how record-playback heads are mounted. Head holes are spirally placed to displace adjacent (circumferentially placed) heads by one track width. The adjustable heads at the top are in recirculating register or revolver loops.

PARALLEL AND SERIAL RECORDING

To ensure accurate clock-pulse identification using this technique, additional clock tracks are often recorded with submultiples of the clock track. In some cases, a single-bit clock track is used to give positive identification of the correct starting point for the clock-track counter.

Fig. 7–16. A typical computer drum with shock mounts and an integral motor. Drum speeds from 2000 to 12,000 rpm are common. Speeds up to 60,000 rpm are under development. (*Courtesy Bryant Computer Products.*)

Let us assume that it is desired to record on a drum the contents of a sixteen-bit binary register. This can be achieved in two ways, parallel or serial. In parallel recording, all sixteen bits are recorded simultaneously, using sixteen tracks and record heads. In serial recording the sixteen bits are recorded sequentially in sixteen data locations, using a single track and head.

In the parallel case, the storage location is selected by the computer program, and when the desired clock bit is detected, all sixteen bits are transferred in parallel from the storage register through the record amplifiers and their respective heads to the surface of the drum. In the serial case, the computer selects the desired starting point, and as each succeeding clock pulse is detected, one of the sixteen bits is transferred from the register to the drum.

Thus the drum's clock track is responsible not only for locating selected storage locations, but also for timing the transfer of information. The contents of the clock-track counter are constantly changing. Whenever the computer addresses the drum, action is called for the first time the counter-stage conditions agree with the address code. The computer might address a location at the exact instant that the corresponding clock-track bit passes its playback head, thus giving instantaneous access to the storage system. However, the desired clock bit may just have passed its playback head, and a complete drum revolution would be required before the desired bit came under it, in which case the access time is equal to the drum's period of revolution. Statistically, the average access time will be half of one drum period, but allowance must be made for the worst case, in which all access times might be equal to the maximum access time or the drum period.

When the computer program calls for the playing back of data, an identical address code is compared with the contents of the clock-track counter, but the record-playback head is now connected to a different kind of amplifier, and the signals it picks up are amplified and applied to an electronic logic circuit that passes only the selected bits of information to the memory output terminals.

RECIRCULATING REGISTERS

In many cases, the delay caused by having to wait for the drum to make a complete revolution is prohibitive. In such cases, *recirculating registers* or *revolver loops* may be employed. By accurately spacing one record and one playback head on a common track, it is possible to recirculate a series of bits at the basic clock frequency. That is to say, the word or words to be stored in this fast-access memory are serially recorded by the record head in normal fashion. By the time the first recorded bit arrives at the playback head, the last bit to be stored has been recorded. The information picked up by the playback head is routed through appropriate amplifiers to the same record head, recirculating the information at a rate determined by the clock frequency and the "length" of the loop.

The recirculating register is similar to the tail-chasing shift register or the acoustic memory except that it combines the simplicity and low cost of the acoustic memory with the permanence and flexibility of the shift register.

When the computer calls for data stored in a recirculating register, the system logic waits for the first bit of the stored word to appear at the loop playback head. The word is then serially routed to the desired location in the system.

RECORDING MODES

Like tape systems, drum recording uses saturation recording of opposite polarity to denote 1's and 0's. The return-to-zero and non-return-to-zero techniques discussed previously are often employed, along with several other recording systems, some of which offer improvements in packing efficiency and reliability.

Drums are available with storage capacities of several million bits. Such systems offer the most economical storage in terms of cost per bit of storage. To improve access times, some work is being done to rotate drums at 60,000 rpm and higher. A 60,000-rpm drum has a maximum access time of 1 millisecond.

A well-constructed drum offers an extremely reliable means of data storage. Where drums must be operated continuously for long periods of time, special construction techniques have been devised wherein the rotating member of the drum literally floats on air. Such *air-bearing* drums can operate almost indefinitely without maintenance.

DISC-FILE MEMORIES

As might be expected, there is a physical limitation in drum size. There are many applications for drum-type storage systems of greater capacity than can be physically realized. To satisfy such requirements, the computer industry has developed several disc-type data systems similar to the familiar juke box with its selectable stack of records.

In these devices, the surface of the discs is used for data storage. One manufacturer moves a single record-playback head set from disc to disc to arrive at a selected storage location. Another manufacturer employs a set of heads for each recording surface, thus eliminating the time lost in positioning the single head and achieving greater simplicity. In the latter case, the heads are moved radially to select the desired tracks and the particular surface is electronically selected by activating the appropriate set of heads. This disc memory provides better than $\frac{1}{2}$ second access to 120,000,000 bits of storage.

Most of the techniques now under development by drum manufacturers are concerned with improvements in mechanical designs that will result in improvements in electrical performance. Closer head-to-drum spacing and new head designs are being investigated to improve packing densities and to raise clock frequencies.

From the foregoing, it will be noticed that most drum systems depend on a clock track for timing. The clock frequency produced by the clock track is usually used throughout the computer to time other operations. In some cases, the drum clock frequency must be *slaved* to a given clock frequency, in which cases elaborate synchronizing systems are employed to slow down or to speed up the drum's rotation to keep the drum's clock in step with the computer's clock.

MAGNETIC-TAPE MEMORIES

Magnetic-tape systems were discussed in Chapter 6 in connection with their use as input-output devices. They also find frequent application as memory systems.

A tape memory system has even greater storage capacity than a drum memory, but the access time is relatively poor, unless the computer program can be written to minimize the time required to search the tape for a selected data-storage location. A typical reel of magnetic tape contains 2500 feet of tape. Packing 200 seven-bit characters per inch, a solid reel of data could conceivably contain 40 million bits. But moving at a typical speed of 75 inches per second, almost 7 minutes will be consumed in passing from one end of the tape to the other. If the data can be stored in approximately the sequence in which they will be used, such access times can be avoided. In some cases, programs are written in such a way that the tape equipment can be "looking for" the next storage location while the computer is busy processing information from the previous location.

· 8 ·

ANALOG COMPUTERS

The most distinguishing characteristic of the analog computer is the *continuous* nature in which it solves problems. Physical phenomena are simulated by electrical or electronic analogs. These are interconnected by the operator or programmer in such a way that all phenomena affecting a physical system are simulated electronically, together with the effects they have on all other parts of the system.

To illustrate by means of an example, consider a gun mounted on top of a hill. At a certain time the gun is fired. The path of the projectile is affected by several factors—the angle of gun elevation, the force of gravity, temperature, wind direction and velocity, shape of the projectile, the type and quantity of propellant used in the gun, the condition of the gun's barrel, and the altitude of the gun. All these factors can be simulated electronically.

ELECTRONIC ANALOGIES

In an analog computer the various electronic analogies are interconnected in such a way that virtually any desired point of information concerning the projectile's flight can be computed.

As an example, it may be of interest to know how high the projectile rises before starting its descent. Or it may be important to know how far the projectile will travel for various angles of gun elevation and propellant charge. In general, it is of interest to compute the effects of different sets of conditions on the performance of the gun.

The analog computer does not produce numbers, as the digital computer does. Most frequently the analog computer produces its results in the form of graphs. In the gun example cited above, the computer might use its graph plotter to trace a curve corresponding to the path of the projectile. In such a case, the position of the mark vertically would correspond to the altitude of the projectile and the distance along the horizontal axis would represent time. Because these two parameters appear in the computer during the simulation of a projectile firing, they can be "looked at" by the computer's plotting equipment. Figure 8–1 shows a typical analog-computer output plotter.

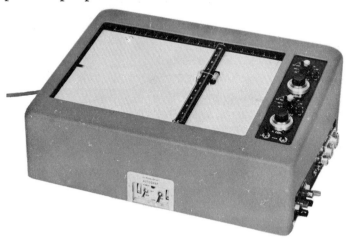

Fig. 8–1. The commonest output device for an analog computer is the x–y plotter, which graphically shows magnitudes of one parameter for various values of any other parameter. (Courtesy F. L. Moseley Co.)

REAL-TIME COMPUTATIONS

In most cases, analog computers are operated in *real time*. That is, the time required for computation is equal to the time consumed by the event being simulated. If we could put a visual indicator (and in fact such provisions are made on analog computers) on the projectile-altitude analog in the computer, we would initially see a voltage corresponding to the initial height of the projectile—the altitude of the gun. Assuming that the gun barrel was pointed upward, this voltage analog would increase quickly, but smoothly, when the gun was fired and would rise to some value corresponding to the peak of its flight. The voltage would then begin to drop off, indicating that the projectile was falling, and it would continue to decrease as the projectile was influenced by gravity.

Somewhere else in the computer is a voltage analogy for projectile velocity and probably one that tells how fast the projectile is losing altitude. All such electronic analogies are connected in the same relationship as their physical counterparts.

Analog computers are often used to investigate complex mechanical systems. Typical systems contain forces and masses that are linked together by such physical phenomena as spring tension, inertia, acceleration, position, and others (see Fig. 8–2).

DEPENDENT AND INDEPENDENT VARIABLES

In a typical study, the analog-computer operator causes one parameter to be altered over a selected range of possible values. This he calls his *independent variable*. Quite often the independent variable is *time*. As in the case of the gun, the gun is fired and the results are displayed for a period of time determined by the programmer. The continuous electronic

Fig. 8–2. A typical commercial analog computer. The four indicators at the top are associated with servo multipliers. Immediately below are thirty-six precision potentiometers that are accessible through the patch panel for use in wiring problems. Below the pots are adjustments for operations amplifiers. The patch panel at the left permits the operator to program the computer to solve specific problems. *(Courtesy Computer Systems.)*

analogs of related parameters show the particular quantities with respect to time. For example, one second after firing, the operator could use a voltmeter to read the altitude of the projectile. Or, he more likely will use the time-history recording scheme described above to give a continuous trace of altitude versus time so that he could later determine altitude at any desired time by measuring the height of the altitude curve.

The various parameters of interest, other than the independent variable, are logically called *dependent variables*, since their values vary and depend on the value of the independent variable. The operator can control the value of his independent variable. He can adjust it manually, and each time he does, corresponding values for the dependent variables appear and can be measured.

OPERATIONAL AMPLIFIERS

The most common type of general-purpose analog computer contains one or more extremely stable electronic amplifiers. Normally the function of an amplifier is to amplify. This is not always the case in analog computers. The main purpose of the analog-computer amplifier, called an *operational amplifier*, is to act as an interconnecting device. The average operational amplifier has several inputs, and its output voltage is proportional to the *sum* of the voltages applied to its inputs.

The last statement may suggest one way in which operational amplifiers are used. They can add, and, because both positive and negative inputs can be applied, the operational amplifier can subtract as well.

Analog-computer operational amplifiers must have extreme stability and gain accuracy, that is, if an amplifier is supposed to have a gain of one (output voltage equals input voltage), it must have a gain as close to one as possible. In addition, its input circuits must be designed so as not to affect the operation of the circuits that feed them. Their output circuits must be designed so they are almost unaffected by the circuits connected to them.

With slight modifications the operational amplifier can serve other functions, such as integration. The importance of this feature will soon become apparent.

The analog computer finds its widest use in solving problems that involve differential equations. Their solution requires considerable finesse when it is done manually. Solution of all but the simplest differential equations is complicated and time-consuming.

DERIVATIVES IN ANALOG COMPUTATION

To gain a modest understanding of derivatives and differential equations, let us consider a few familiar physical phenomena. We can readily visualize the mile as a unit of distance. We are also familiar with such units as feet, yards, meters, etc. Because of our constant association with automobiles, airplanes, and other vehicles, we are also familiar with the *first time derivative* of distance. We call it *speed* or *velocity*. Velocity is the *rate of change of distance*. We say that a vehicle is moving at a *rate* of 60 miles per hour.

If someone asks us how far the vehicle will travel in 1 hour, we immediately answer 60 miles. In so doing, we are solving a form of differential equation.

Going one step deeper into the field of derivatives, what name can we assign to the *rate of change of the rate of change of distance*? This sounds difficult, but it is a term we use every day. This *second time derivative of distance* is *acceleration*. When we say "speed up" or "slow down" we mean increase or decrease the vehicle's rate of travel, or velocity.

If we were told that a vehicle was accelerating at a rate of 60 miles per hour per hour, we could calculate the speed at any time, provided that we knew the vehicle's initial speed. If we knew the initial starting point, we could also calculate the distance the vehicle traveled from its origin at any given time. In solving such problems, we are solving a form of *second-order differential equation.*

INTEGRATION

Let us see how an analog computer can aid in performing such computations. In answering the question, "How far does a vehicle travel in an hour if it is traveling at 60 miles per hour?" we say quickly 60 miles. We are performing the process of *integration.* To do this electronically, we must produce an electrical quantity that is continuously proportional to velocity and that will provide a means to accumulate or to integrate this quantity for the desired period of time. At all times during the solution, this quantity will be proportional to the distance traveled.

The input to the integrating amplifier is a voltage that is proportional to the rate of change of a quantity with respect to time. The output is a voltage that is proportional to the quantity itself and is constantly changing when the input is other than zero.

To relate acceleration to position, it is necessary to perform a double integration. This is readily achieved by connecting two integrators in tandem. A signal proportional to acceleration is applied to the first integrator. Its output is proportional to velocity and can be applied to the second integrator, whose output represents distance.

ANALOG MULTIPLICATION

Two different techniques are employed by analog computers to perform multiplication and division. One uses an electromechanical system comprised of precision components. These are called *servo multipliers*. Voltages proportional to the two quantities to be multiplied are applied to appropriate input terminals and the product appears (with some delay) at the output terminal. The output is delayed somewhat because of the mechanical inertia of the system.

A simplified diagram of a servo multiplier is shown in Fig. 8–3. The potentiometer slider is positioned by one of the quantities being multiplied, and the other quantity is applied to the top of the potentiometer resistance element. The voltage that appears at the slider represents the product of the two quantities. If the first input increases, the slider is moved toward the high voltage end of the resistance element, increasing the output. An increase in the second input will cause an output increase by raising the voltage that is applied to the resistance element.

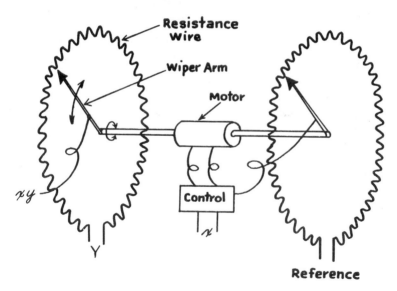

Fig. 8–3.   One commonly used device in analog-computer systems is the servo multiplier. Voltages proportional to *x* and *y* are applied to the inputs and the output is proportional to the product of the two.

The other type of multiplier employs electronic techniques and is much faster. However, as might be expected, a price must be paid for this speed in both complexity and cost, and accuracy is also sacrificed.

FUNCTION GENERATION

Analog problems often involve relationships that cannot conveniently be expressed in terms of a formula or an equation, or by simply multiplying, dividing, adding, or subtracting. When these appear together in a problem, they can be tied together by means of an analog technique known as *function generation*. The conventional function generator has an input terminal and an output terminal. A signal applied to the input causes a signal to appear at the output in accordance with the particular relationship involved. In some cases, the input and output may seem completely unrelated. This input-output relationship is under the control of the operator and is usually adjusted manually in accordance with experimentally derived or calculated information.

As an example, temperatures are often measured by the use of thermocouples. The thermocouple has the property of producing a voltage when heated. In general, the more heat, the more voltage. But, the relationship between temperature and voltage is not *linear*, nor are the two phenomena related in such a way that one can be obtained from the other by means of a simple formula. (That is, if 1 millivolt represents 100 degrees, 2 millivolts will not necessarily represent 200 degrees, and so on.)

The operator of a computer involving such a relationship refers to curves furnished by the manufacturers of the thermocouples that give actual temperatures for each value of voltage (see Fig. 8–4). He uses this information to set up a function generator. Once the desired function has been set,

Fig. 8–4. A typical analog-computer installation shows the operator watching the plotter as the computer solves a problem programmed on the patch panel in the center of the main console. *(Courtesy Electronic Associates, Inc.)*

any input signal (proportional to thermocouple voltage) will cause an output signal that is proportional to temperature.

Several different types of function generators are in common use today. All represent compromises in speed and accuracy. The most-common type is called the *diode-function generator*. This device essentially breaks up the input signal into segments. For voltages falling within each segment, adjustable modifications are applied to the input to achieve the desired output. By adjusting potentiometers, the operator can position the lines of demarcation between segments and can also adjust the degree of modification that is applied for each segment.

ELECTROMECHANICAL FUNCTION GENERATION

Another type of function generator employs an electromechanical plotting device to generate arbitrary functions. The surface of a table is covered with a piece of graph paper with increments marked off along the horizontal axis in units of x and the verticle axis in units of y. The relationship between these two parameters can be expressed by means of a curve, which in this case is drawn on the paper using conductive ink (ink capable of conducting electrical current).

If we chose x as the independent variable (or the input, which is under the control of the operator or the computer), we select values for x and determine the corresponding values for y by moving vertically from the chosen values of x until we reach the curve, then moving horizontally to the y axis where we read the value of y.

This can be done electronically with the result that values for y are continuously applied to the output terminals for all values of x applied to the input terminal.

The *curve-follower* function generator employs electronic and electromechanical servo techniques. First the head is positioned horizontally along the x axis to a physical position proportional to the value of x. The head is controlled vertically by another positioning system that comes to rest only when the head is touching the conductive ink of the curve. A voltage that is proportional to the resulting vertical displacement of the head is produced as an output.

This system has the advantage of being able to produce a large variety of functions with a relatively simple means for changing functions and with a high degree of resolution. It has the disadvantage of being severely limited with respect to time, owing to the mechanical inertia of the moving parts.

Analog computers can be used to process data from external sources or they can be used strictly with manually in-

serted data. In the latter case, the various electrical analogies
are interconnected by means of a patch panel.

TYPICAL PROBLEM AND SOLUTION

In addition to making provisions for connecting various
amplifiers together, the patch panel provides for the estab-
lishment of *initial conditions* for a particular problem. To illustrate the use of initial conditions and patch-panel programming, consider the simple mechanical system illustrated in
Fig. 8–5. This system consists of a weight W suspended from
a fixed ceiling by means of a spring whose spring constant
(degree of springiness) is k. The formula relating the various
parameters involved is a second-order differential equation

$$\frac{d^2x}{dt^2} = -kx$$

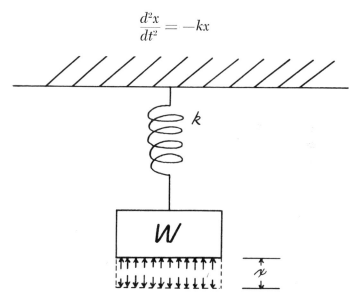

Fig. 8–5.   A simple mechanical system involving a spring and a weight
can be thoroughly analyzed using analog-computer techniques. A block
diagram showing the relationship between parameters is shown in
Fig. 8–7.

This equation says that if the weight is displaced by a distance x (from the position where the system would come to rest if allowed sufficient time) the subsequent positions (or values of x) will bear the above relationship to time.

Intuitively, we would expect the weight to bounce up and down, or oscillate, with the oscillations becoming smaller and smaller until the system comes to rest. Solution of the equation will bear out this prediction, whether it be done manually by setting into the equation different values of t (for time) and plotting the result, or by a computer that automatically produces at its output continuous values for x as t increases from zero to the time required for the system to achieve equilibrium.

ANALOG-COMPUTER SYMBOLS

Figure 8–6 shows a compilation of symbols commonly used to identify analog-computer components, together with equations relating the input and output of each device. Figure 8–7 shows the analog-computer solution for the problem posed by the mechanical system illustrated in Fig. 8–5.

Here we see how initial conditions are established. Any signal applied to the input of integrating amplifier "1" will be interpreted as acceleration. On the computer patch panel, provisions are made for introducing any desired voltage to the input of the integrator, in addition to the input which "closes the loop" on the equation by substituting for the equality sign. If the weight is not at rest at the beginning of the problem, an initial velocity can be applied to the input of integrator 2.

Attenuator k is a potentiometer that attenuates the value x according to the springiness of the spring. It can be set for different values. simply by twisting a multiple-turn dial, thereby permitting study of the system with different springs.

If the desired result from this problem is a picture of the position of the weight from the beginning until the system comes to rest, a recorder can be attached to either line marked x. The chart paper is placed in motion some time before the problem is initiated. The deflection of the recorder writing pen is adjusted to represent deflection x. At the beginning of the problem, the deflection of the pen will be equal

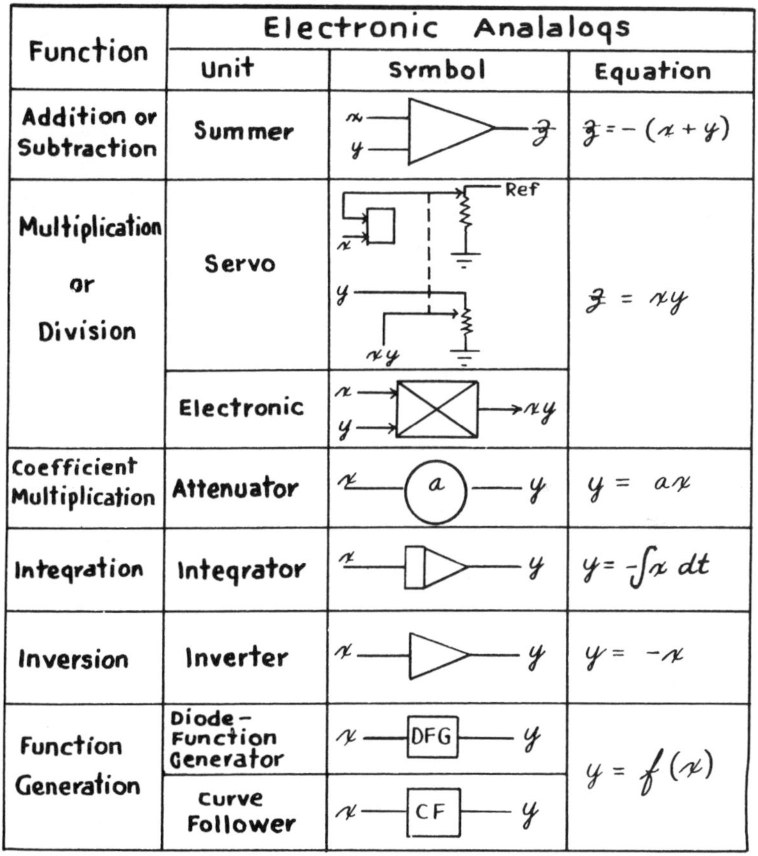

Function
Electronic Analalogs
Unit
Symbol
Equation
Addition or Subtraction
Summer
x
y
z
z = −(x + y)
Multiplication or Division
Servo
Ref
x
y
xy
z = xy
Electronic
x
y
xy
Coefficient Multiplication
Attenuator
x
a
y
y = ax
Integration
Integrator
x
y
y = −∫x dt
Inversion
Inverter
x
y
y = −x
Function Generation
Diode-Function Generator
x
DFG
y
Curve Follower
x
CF
y
y = f(x)

Fig. 8–6. Typical symbols used in mapping analog-computer problems.

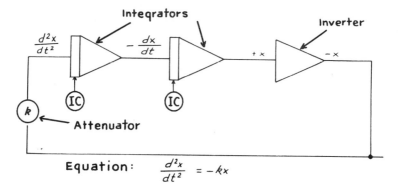

Fig. 8–7.   An analog-computer method of solving problems involving the simple mechanical system illustrated in Fig. 8–6. Circles marked IC are used to establish initial conditions, for example, in cases where weight has a finite acceleration or velocity when the problem is begun.

to the initial condition of x. When the weight is released (electronically speaking), x decreases toward zero (equilibrium). In the mechanical system the inertia of the weight causes the *sign* of x to change, that is, the weight passes through the equilibrium point until gravity or increased spring tension causes the excursion to reverse. The recorder pen produces a cyclic (sinusoidal) curve with respect to time, giving a complete *time history* of the system.

In some types of analog computers, results are displayed on oscilloscopes similar to television picture tubes. In such cases, the problem is actually solved over and over again at a rate so fast that the oscilloscope trace appears to be a continuous line. This method of analog computation has several advantages. Results are immediately available for all possible conditions and various parameters can be adjusted with immediate display of their effect on the dependent variables. This technique, however, has lower accuracy. Each type of analog computer has its optimum kind of application.

Fig. 8–8.   This special-purpose analog computer has no patch panel because the single problem is prewired. This MidCentury unit solves problems that involve conversion of various types of radar information.

SPECIAL-PURPOSE ANALOG COMPUTERS

Analog computation is used in various special-purpose applications that do not require the accuracy of digital computation. A special-purpose analog computer for solving radar problems is shown in Fig. 8–8. Some mechanical analog computers have been built to solve problems of tremendous complexity, such as aircraft-navigation problems. A typical mechanical computer of this type is shown in Fig. 8–9.

Fig. 8–9. A typical electro-mechanical analog computer used to solve aircraft-navigation problems. (*Courtesy Hoffman Electronics.*)

· 9 ·

DATA-ACQUISITION SYSTEMS

Aircraft and missile designers depend heavily upon computers for assistance with their design calculations and in evaluating test results. In previous portions of this book, many ways were discussed for the specialists to ask the computer for assistance in solving design equations. They set up their equations, and a programmer codes the necessary input information and instructions or commands and monitors the operation of the machine until the desired results are obtained.

In evaluation of tests the problem is often quite different. Sometimes such tests are conducted in a wind tunnel or in a laboratory where wing sections and other parts of the vehicle can be tested to destruction, if desired, by loading them with sandbags or otherwise subjecting them to varying degrees of stress and strain. In other cases, tests are performed by actually flying the vehicle, in which cases, test data must be telemetered to the data-acquisition site, unless the vehicle can be recovered and carry its own data-acquisition and recording equipment.

DATA-SYSTEM REQUIREMENTS

The data-acquisition problem is usually complicated by the conflicting requirements for sampling test data: (1) very often, (2) very accurately, and (3) at a large number of test points. In addition, data must be accumulated in such a manner that the computer or data-processing equipment can accept and understand it. So the ideal data-acquisition system should sample the data as often as possible, as accurately as possible, and it should have as its end product the data stored in such a form that it can be applied to a digital computer for processing.

Sources of data usually take the form of some kind of transducer. A transducer is any device that converts a physical phenomenon into a measurable analogy. In a given data-acquisition system, many different types of transducers may be used. Typical information that may be of interest includes rotation or shaft position, voltage, current, pressure, force, strain, lateral motion, temperature, flow, and acceleration. For maximum efficiency in high-speed data processing, these parameters must be converted into digital form automatically.

SHAFT-TO-DIGITAL CONVERTERS

In the case of shaft position, a variety of *shaft-to-digital converters* are commercially available. A simplified version is illustrated in Fig. 9–1. We have seen how a computer can interpret combinations of switch closures. In the shaft-to-digital converter illustrated, four bits (brush contacting metal or insulator determining switch closure or open circuit) describe the position of the shaft to an accuracy of one part in sixteen. As the shaft is rotated the code changes, and a computer or buffering device can obtain position information by interrogating the four terminals. By adding a fifth "track" that has twice as many segments as the least significant (outside) track in the previous example, the resolution of measurement is doubled. With a sixth track it is quadrupled, and so on. Some of these devices are accurate to one part in several tens of thousands.

The simple shaft-to-digital converter illustrated in Fig. 9–1 is actually of little value. First, its resolution is extremely

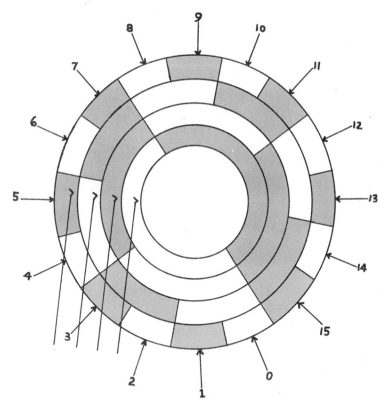

Fig. 9–1. Shaft encoders are commonly used to convert analog-shaft-position information to digital form for automatic high-speed data processing. The simple encoder system shown produces a different code for each of sixteen shaft positions.

poor. Second, there is always the possibility that the computer will interrogate the device at a time when an erroneous reading is appearing at the output. To explain, the brush contacts cannot be perfectly aligned, nor can the edges of the metallic segments. Thus the possibility exists that the 8's brush could lag behind the others slightly. In passing from position 15 to position 0 this lag would cause a brief period when the reading is 8 (the 8's brush still in contact) giving a 180 degree (half a turn) error.

To avoid errors of this sort, and errors of several less-obvious origins, practical shaft digitizers employ many different techniques, such as special codes, dual-brush systems, and systems with logic to inhibit interrogation when a transition is taking place.

INCREMENTAL SHAFT DIGITIZERS

Another type of shaft digitizer is called the *incremental* type. Figure 9–2 shows a simplified incremental shaft dig-

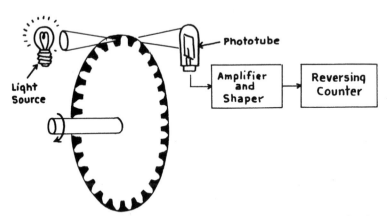

Fig. 9–2. An incremental shaft-position digitizer produces a pulse for every increment of shaft rotation. External reversing counters keep track of the shaft position by counting pulses and adding for one direction and subtracting for the opposite direction.

itizer. In this case, the digitizer produces an electrical impulse each time it is rotated by a certain increment. To keep track of shaft position with this type, an external counter is required. One complication is the necessity to keep track of the *direction* of rotation. Pulses created by rotating the shaft in one direction are added, whereas pulses created by rotation in the opposite direction must be subtracted from the counter. Reversing counters and special logic systems for differentiating between forward and backward pulses have been developed and are commercially available.

Shaft position is one of the few parameters that can be converted directly into digital form. More often an intermediate form of information is required.

VOLTAGE ANALOGS

In the measurement of temperatures the *thermocouple* is widely used. The thermocouple is a tiny junction of two dissimilar metals. Because of the way in which these metals are joined, a minute voltage will appear across their junction. Fortunately, the magnitude of this voltage is roughly proportional to the temperature of the junction. Because the thermocouple is extremely small, it has relatively low thermal inertia (that is, it heats up and cools off quickly), and thus it will rapidly assume the temperature of a body to which it is attached. Thus by measuring the thermocouple voltage and by referring to calibration data obtained from subjecting the thermocouple to known temperatures, the temperature of a body can be determined. Typical thermocouple signals have magnitudes of a few thousandths of a volt or millivolts.

Pressure is measured in many ways. The most frequently encountered method (for automatic data-acquisition systems) utilizes a *strain-gage transducer*. The pressure being measured is applied to one surface of a diaphragm that has a deflection that bears some relationship to the applied pressure. To measure the deflection (and thus the pressure) a strain gage is used. This is a device made up of very thin wires whose electrical properties are modified by physical deformation. Normally a reference voltage is applied to the gage. The change in electrical properties resulting from pressure changes produces varying output voltage, which is related to the pressure applied to the gage.

Potentiometers are frequently used to convert lineal motion to voltage information for a data-acquisition system. Referring to Fig. 9–3, the lateral motion being monitored is coupled through a gearing system to a potentiometer which consists of a resistance element and a slider. The farther the arm moves, the higher the voltage "picked off" by the wiper arm. Thus again we have a voltage that is related to the parameter of interest, in this case, motion or position.

From the foregoing discussion of transducers, it should be obvious that most physical parameters can readily be expressed in terms of voltage. Because the goal of a data-acquisition system is to process such information in a digital

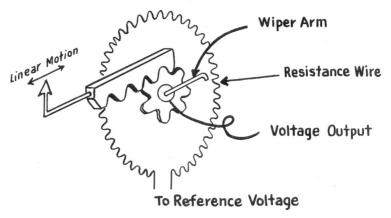

Fig. 9–3.   Linear motion can be converted into proportional voltage using the simple mechanical system shown. Linear motion rotates the wiper of the potentiometer, which in turn picks off more or less of the reference voltage depending upon its position.

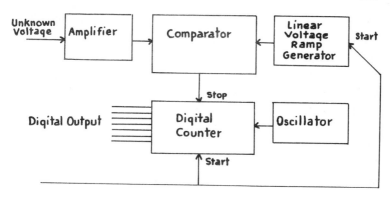

Fig. 9–4. A ramp-type analog(voltage)-to-digital converter uses a voltage ramp and a timing mechanism to measure an unknown voltage. The reading on the digital counter corresponds to the voltage when the coincidence between them is unknown and the ramp is detected.

computer, some means of converting voltage to digital form is required.

DIGITAL VOLTMETERS

One way to convert voltage to digital information is to use a *ramp-type digital voltmeter*. A simplified block diagram of this type of instrument is shown in Fig. 9–4. The heart of this system is a circuit that produces a linear voltage ramp, or a point where the voltage is increasing by some fixed amount during each increment of time. The purpose of this is to generate a constantly increasing voltage that will sweep across the anticipated input voltage to be measured in some exact time interval.

Comparing this internally generated voltage with the unknown input voltage, a point will be reached where the two are equal, provided the input voltage is within the range of the ramp. The time at which this coincidence occurs will depend on the magnitude of the input voltage. Because the ramp begins at the lowest part of the range and increases linearly, the time from start of the ramp to coincidence is directly proportional to the unknown voltage.

Time interval is relatively simple to digitize. A typical ramp-type digital voltmeter uses a crystal-controlled 1-megacycle oscillator (1 million cycles per second) to generate 1-microsecond (1 millionth of a second) timing increments. The increments are electronically counted until coincidence is obtained, at which time the digital counter has stored in it a number proportional to the input voltage. This counter (consisting of flip-flops) can be interrogated by external equipment in a data-acquisition system and can be stored in a form suitable for computer entry.

By proper choice of ramp angle, the digital output can be made to define the input voltage directly in volts. For example, consider a system in which the voltage ramp has a slope of 1 volt for every millisecond. If the oscillator operates

Fig. 9–5. A commercial digital voltmeter using the principle illustrated in Fig. 9–4. This unit, manufactured by Epsco, Inc., can perform 100 analog-to-digital conversions per second to an accuracy of 0.1 per cent. It also digitizes resistances and alternating current voltages. (*Courtesy Epsco, Inc.*)

at 1 kilocycle (1000 cycles per second), each oscillator output pulse represents 1 millisecond and, consequently, 1 volt. For an input voltage of 45 volts, for example, the ramp would require 45 milliseconds to reach coincidence with the input, and the counter, counting 1-millisecond increments, would be stopped at coincidence with a count of 45.

Ramp-type digital voltmeters are limited in speed and accuracy by the circuitry required to generate the linear voltage ramp. Typical electronic units can achieve 100 conversions per second with accuracies of 0.1 per cent. Figure 9–5 shows a typical commercial unit of this type.

HIGH-SPEED ANALOG-TO-DIGITAL CONVERTERS

Many applications require greater speed and accuracy. Figure 9–6 shows a voltage-to-digital converter that has been used commercially in quantity production to perform as many as 50,000 conversions per second, each conversion having an accuracy of 0.05 per cent, or 1 part in 2000.

This technique is called *successive approximation,* and in some respects it approaches a special-purpose computer in speed of operation and use of logic elements. The simplified version shown in Fig. 9–7 shows mechanical switches, but in the actual units everything is electronic. Each step takes only 2 microseconds.

To illustrate, assume a voltage input range of 0 to 15 volts. Also assume that the input amplifier has the capability of producing a current I_x that is equal in milliamperes to the input voltage in volts. The switches associated with the 15-volt standard are arranged so that I_8 introduces 8 milliamperes into the summer, switch I_4 introduces 4 milliamperes, switch I_2 introduces 2 milliamperes, and I_1 introduces 1 milliampere.

The comparator is arranged to produce an output signal whenever the sum of currents I_s exceeds the input current I_x.

Fig. 9–6. Where extreme speed is required, the successive-approximation approach is used for analog-to-digital conversion. The unit shown performs as many as 44,000 conversions per second to an accuracy of 0.05 per cent.

Let us assume an input of slightly more than 5 volts, which would cause I_x to be slightly more than 5 milliamperes. The electronic programmer first closes switch I_8, causing a current of 8 milliamperes to be introduced into the summer. Because this current alone exceeds the 5-milliampere input current, the programmer receives a pulse from the comparator that it uses to open switch I_8. Next the programmer closes switch I_4, introducing 4 milliamperes into the summer. This does *not* exceed the input current, so no comparator output pulse is generated. The programmer then leaves the 4-milliampere current switch closed and closes switch I_2, introducing an additional 2 milliamperes of current into the summer. Because the sum of 2 and 4 is 6, and exceeds 5, the comparator produces an output which is used by the programmer to open switch I_2. Finally switch I_1 is closed, and because the sum of 4 and 1 does not exceed the input (which was slightly higher than 5), no output from the comparator is detected.

Thus the final position of the switches represents the digital (binary) value of the input voltage and can be interrogated by external equipment. A converter of this type can employ as many as eleven binary-weighted current switches to achieve a measuring or conversion accuracy of 1 part in 2048, or approximately 0.05 per cent. By using current weights in binary-coded decimal progression, conversions from voltage to binary-coded decimal can be obtained.

It should be noted that successive-approximation digitizing always consumes the same amount of time, and with the same type of circuitry, the time required for one conversion is dependent only on the number of bits or comparator de-

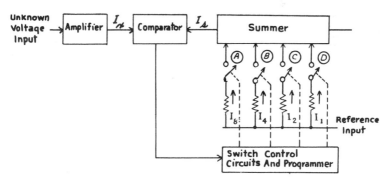

Fig. 9–7. A four-bit successive-approximation analog-to-digital converter. Practical units employ as many as thirteen bits, binary-coded. Each conversion requires the same amount of time, regardless of the value of the unknown.

cisions required to obtain the desired accuracy and resolution.

MULTIPLEXING

A voltage-to-digital converter is a single-channel device,
that is, at any one time it can accept one input voltage and a
short time thereafter have available at its output the appropriate digital code representing the input voltage.

Because most data-acquisition systems require the measurement of a multiplicity of unknown voltages, a method of
presenting them sequentially to the digitizer must be devised.
This process is called *multiplexing.* A simplified schematic
representation of a mechanical multiplexer is shown in Fig.
9–8. As the switch is rotated it is allowed to dwell on each
input long enough for the digitizer to perform the required
analog-to-digital conversion. The digitizer is automatically
reset to zero before embarking on each new conversion cycle.

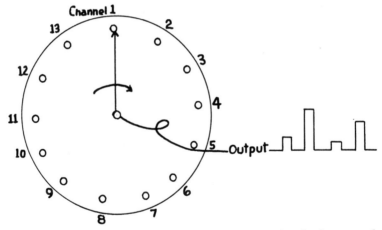

Fig. 9–8.   Mechanical analogy shows the function of multiplexers used
in high-speed data-acquisition systems. Some multiplexers are electronic
and permit switching and digitizing rates as high as 25,000 samples per
second.

Even the fastest mechanical multiplexers have serious speed limitations for many applications. As a result, electronic multiplexers have been developed that can switch input channels at rates as high as 25,000 per second, allowing sufficient dwell time for a high-speed digitizer to convert each input to digital form.

With such speeds, even rapidly changing parameters can be measured with sufficient time resolution to enable the data-processing computer to perform computations that involve the cross correlation (comparison of trends in one parameter with respect to another) of collected data. However, successive inputs will be displaced in time by the period of time required for the multiplexer switching and conversion. When this time displacement is undesirable, a technique known as *sample-and-hold* multiplexing is used.

In sample-and-hold multiplexing the multiplexer samples all input channels simultaneously and holds the respective voltages long enough for the converter to digitize each stored quantity in turn. This technique is also used when input data are changing so rapidly that erroneous values, caused by a variation of I_x into the comparator during a conversion cycle, might result.

RECORDING DIGITAL DATA

It should be noted that all the while the multiplexer and digitizer are going through the process described above, digital information is appearing at regular intervals at the output terminals of the analog-to-digital converter. Normally, this information appears as one voltage level on all output terminals associated with 1 bits and no voltage on all output terminals associated with 0 bits. The correct code appears only when all successive approximations have been made. It disappears when the converter is reset to make the next conversion.

Thus the correct code appears at the output terminals in the form of voltage levels at the end of each conversion for a brief period of time. Gating circuitry like that described in Chapter 5 is used to transfer this digital information to the output display or storage device.

If a data-acquisition system like that described above is operated continuously over a period of time, some means must be provided to prepare its output for computer entry. Earlier it was shown that computers take in information in bunches or blocks, each block containing a number of individual measurements. On magnetic tape, such blocks must usually be separated physically by a gap on the tape to permit the tape-handling mechanism reading the information into the computer to start and to stop without losing information.

TAPE FORMATTING

To create such blocks and to accommodate the many other computer format requirements, equipment like that shown in Fig. 9–9 is commonly used. The continuous digital data being produced by the converter are "pumped" into memory A at a rate determined by the converter and multiplexer system. When memory A is filled, the digital input is automatically routed to memory B and the emptying cycle of memory A is begun.

The emptying onto magnetic tape is accomplished at a greater speed than the filling, so the data stored in memory A is transferred to the tape before memory B is filled. The tape may continue to run, however, with the result that by the time memory B is filled and ready for emptying onto the tape, a gap has been generated on the magnetic tape that is sufficiently long to permit the computer tape mechanism to start and stop between blocks.

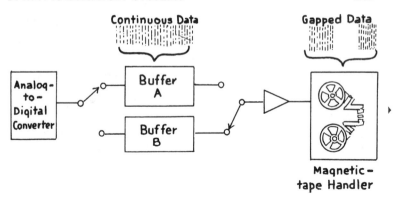

Fig. 9–9. Digital data being produced continuously by analog-to-digital converter are bunched before recording on magnetic tape, which produces a gap between blocks of data so that the computer can accept data in bursts and stop between bursts.

INFORMATION THEORY

No discussion of data-acquisition systems would be complete without some mention of information theory. Some data change faster than other data. For example, if a beam is flexed back and forth at a rapid rate, the stresses and strains are rapidly varying and a signal proportional to these parameters has a cycle form, and fluctuations occur at the same rate as the flexing. It may be of interest to study the heating effect of such flexing. In such a case, it would be found that the temperature rise, measured anywhere on the beam, would be extremely slow compared with the other data changes.

Theoretically, these two types of parameters would not necessarily have to be sampled the same number of times during a test. Possibly if the same rates were employed, the slower-changing temperature measurement would go unchanged for several cycles of the strain information, thus wasting measurements. The temperature rise requires relatively few samples, but the strain signals require very fre-

quent sampling to give the computer a clear picture of what
has happened.

Authorities disagree on the number of times a cyclic signal must be sampled to preserve a given degree of accuracy.
Many factors must be considered in arriving at such a number. In general, any system that samples a fluctuating input
signal several times for each fluctuation is considered adequate for most data-processing purposes.

REAL-TIME COMPUTATION

In some computer applications, it is important to perform a required computation immediately upon making a
measurement. This is particularly true of process-control
computers; in these a certain parameter is controlled by controlling related functions according to a computed function.

In such cases, the output of the analog-to-digital converter is fed directly into the input register of the computer.
Many general-purpose computers have provisions for accepting data in this fashion. Computations of this type are called
real-time computations.

Many special-purpose computers operate in this fashion
(see Fig. 9–10). A missile-guidance computer, for example,
constantly "looks at" acceleration transducers and makes
necessary changes in its guidance system to make the transducer readings agree with those anticipated for a given
course. In the process-control field, an entirely new type of
digital computer utilizing real-time computation based on
constant-input-data samples, has recently been developed.

TELEMETRY SYSTEMS

In any data-acquistion system, the source of data and
the acquisition system may be separated physically. For example, a link is required in aircraft testing because the data-

Fig. 9–10. A data-acquisition system installed at Republic Aviation Corporation digitizes the outputs of 200 assorted transducers and prepares resulting digital data in a form suitable for direct entry into a commercial digital computer via magnetic tape.

gathering equipment may be too bulky and heavy to be flown. In such cases, radio telemetry is often used. Telemetry in other forms, via land lines for example, serves to transport information from source to data-acquisition site or directly to the computer.

Frequency-modulation telemetry involves the transmission of radio signals whose frequency components bear a known relationship with parameters measured at the source. The resulting signals are unscrambled at the data-processing site, and the original data are converted into computer language.

Another popular form of telemetry employs a technique known as *pulse-duration modulation*. Here the measured parameters cause proportionally shaped pulses of radio-frequency energy to be transmitted to the receiving station for unscrambling, digitizing, and conversion to computer language. One feature of this system is its ability to accommodate many channels of information and to transmit, along with the measured data, information for calibrating the airborne-measuring equipment at regular intervals.

Both of these systems are limited in speed and accuracy. A more-advanced system, known as *pulse-code modulation,* employs an airborne analog-to-digital converter and multiplexer. Instead of telemetering analog information and suffering the degradation of data caused by fading and noise, only digital information is transmitted. Because digital information consists of two-state 1's and 0's and because these can be differentiated with relative ease even in the presence of fading and noise, the digital system is more accurate.

· 10 ·

TYPICAL COMPUTER SYSTEMS

Although the computer industry is in its infancy, it is already highly competitive. As in most fields, a few leaders are far out in front, but the relative positions of the leaders and challengers are constantly shifting as new designs are announced and existing systems are expanded or modified to meet the changing requirements of the users.

It is difficult to categorize digital computers. A so-called "small" computer can incorporate so much peripheral equipment that it rivals "large" computers in cost and performance. However, omitting such cases, it is possible to draw a rather indefinite line of demarcation between the "small" and the "large" systems.

A large percentage of the computers in use today are either rented or leased, but for purposes of comparison, only approximate selling prices will be considered. In general, computers costing more than $250,000 can be considered in the large-system category; those costing less qualify as small systems. Some small electronic computers sell for less than $10,000, but some large systems carry price tags in the multi-million-dollar region.

Computer installations are seldom alike. Aside from differences in peripheral equipment, physical layout may change to accommodate emphasis on particular types of activity. Some centers employ several small systems to do the same work that one large system does elsewhere.

One of the most significant "internal" differences between one system and another involves the amount and type of storage that is contained in the internal fast-access memory system. A small computer with a large memory can become a powerful system in spite of its "size." But the larger systems, in addition to speed and flexibility, often offer advantages in programming ease and similar operational benefits.

The Model 650 computer manufactured by IBM is probably the most common system in use today (see Fig. 10–1). More than a thousand are in operation. The 650 falls into the "small" category, but, fitted with typical peripheral equip-

Fig. 10–1. One of the more popular medium-sized electronic data-processing machines is the IBM 650. Card input and output is generally employed, but magnetic tape is offered as an option.

ment, it quickly joins the large systems in both cost and capability. It is used about equally for business and scientific data processing.

Physically, the main portion of the IBM 650 is approximately the size of a large "Coke" machine. Various memory systems and input-output devices are available.

The 650 can handle words of ten digits plus sign. Two basic memory systems are available. A fast-access core memory is capable of storing and providing fast access to sixty computer words. A medium-speed drum memory provides better than 100-microsecond access to 2000 additional computer words. An optional random-access memory is available for storing up to 40,000 groups of 690 digits each.

The IBM 650 requires from 2 to 20 milliseconds to perform multiplication of two ten-digit numbers, 6 to 23 milliseconds for division. Addition requires approximately 700 microseconds. It can store up to ninety-six instructions.

Input and output are normally achieved by means of punch cards at rates of eighty words per second using three card-handling machines. An optional magnetic-tape unit increases the input-data rate to 1174 words per second. Selling prices of IBM 650 systems range from $200,000 to $1,000,000.

The IBM 704 system also serves both scientific and business users, but it is capable of much greater speed, accuracy, and flexibility than the 650. Together with a typical collection of input, output, and memory equipment, a 704 system fills a large room (see Fig. 10–2).

The 704 can handle both binary-coded decimal words (like the 650) and thirty-six-bit straight binary words. Several internal-memory systems are available. Providing 12-microsecond access are optional core memories of 4000, 8000, and 32,000 words. Also available is a 16,000-word magnetic-drum memory. As many as ten magnetic-tape units may be used as a medium-speed internal memory, providing additional storage capacity.

Fig. 10–2. The IBM 704 is widely used to process data for both scientific and business applications.

The IBM 704 requires 24 microseconds to perform addition and 240 microseconds to perform multiplication or division. Provisions are made for storing up to eighty-six instructions. Input-output rates via magnetic tape may be as high as 2500 words per second. This popular system carries a selling price of $1,000,000 to $2,500,000.

Rapidly gaining popularity in business and scientific applications are the IBM 705 and 709 systems. These are produced in various models, depending upon storage and input-output requirements. One version of the 705 can use up to thirty magnetic drums, each capable of storing 60,000 characters. As many as 100 magnetic-tape units can be employed. Input-output rates as high as 62,500 characters per second for one tape unit are realizable. The 709 can perform multiplication and division in as little as 24 microseconds, and it is available with various memory combinations. Prices of these two systems range from $1,000,000 to $4,000,000 and higher.

Not all computers carry such high price tags. An extremely popular and useful machine is the Bendix G–15 (see Fig. 10–3). This small system is intended for business and scientific work. It employs eight-character binary-coded decimal words. Input-output rates as high as 430 characters per second are obtainable. Addition can be achieved in 430 microseconds, and 16.7 milliseconds is required for multiplication and division. Both magnetic-tape and perforated-tape memory and input-output equipment are available. Up to fifty instructions with 1300 variations can be stored. The G–15 sells for approximately $50,000.

Fig. 10–3.   The Bendix G–15 computer is one of the more widely used "small" electronic computers. Up to four magnetic-tape handlers may be used.

Fig. 10–4.   The ElectroData Division of Burroughs offers the Model 205 in the medium-sized-computer field.

The ElectroData Division of the Burroughs Corporation offers several systems, among which is the Model 205 (see Fig. 10–4). This system employs an eleven-character word. Rapid-access memory is in the form of a magnetic drum capable of storing over 4000 words. Magnetic tape may be used to store an additional 200 million words. Addition time is less than 2 milliseconds, multiplication can be achieved in 8 milliseconds, and division can be achieved in 10 milliseconds. Up to seventy-one instructions can be stored, and input-output rates via magnetic tape are 600 words per second. Selling prices range from $150,000 to $350,000.

The newer and larger ElectroData Model 220 (see Fig. 10–5) also employs eleven-digit words. Core memories of 2000 to 10,000 words with 10-microsecond access time are available. An additional 55 million words can be stored on magnetic tape. Addition, multiplication, and division times are 180 microseconds, 2.1 milliseconds, and 4 milliseconds, respectively. Magnetic-tape input-output rates of 2400 words per second are provided. These systems sell for $250,000 to nearly $1,000,000.

The Royal McBee LGP-30 is a popular version of a small machine comparing in size, shape, and weight to a typical home freezer (see Fig. 10–6). Intended for business and scientific use, it employs words of five alphanumeric or nine numeric characters. Three core registers are provided for fast-access storage and a magnetic drum provides storage of up to 4096 words with a maximum access time of 17 milliseconds. Addition time is 260 milliseconds. Up to sixteen instructions can be stored. The input-output rates are 30 words per second via perforated tape. The selling price is $50,000.

One of the newer and most successful entries into the rapidly growing computer field is the Philco Model S-2000

Fig. 10–5. The ElectroData Model 220 features a wide variety of high-speed paper- and magnetic-tape input-output equipment.

Fig. 10–6.   Royal McBee's LGP–30 is one of the more-versatile low-cost computers. Entirely self-contained, it is capable of moderate speeds with simple programming.

Fig. 10–7.   Philco's Transac is a completely transistorized, very high-speed computer that has recently been widely accepted by the industry. Many storage and input-output options are offered.

Transac computer for business and scientific applications (see Fig. 10–7). Words of forty-eight bits are employed (straight binary or six-bit alphanumeric binary-coded decimal). Core-memory systems of 4096 words are standard. Expansion to 65,536 words is possible. A magnetic drum having a 32,768-word storage capacity is also available, and as many as thirty-two drums may be employed in a single system! Addition times as low as 18 microseconds are achievable, and multiplication and division can be done in as little as 51 micro-seconds. The S-2000 can store over 200 instructions and input-output rates as high as 90,000 characters per second are available using magnetic tape. Selling prices for the Transac start at $1,000,000.

The RCA 501 system (see Fig. 10–8) can handle words of almost unlimited size using seven bits per alphanumeric character. Rapid-access core memories of 16,384 to 262,144 characters with 15-microsecond access can be provided. In addition, as many as sixty-three magnetic-tape stations can be accommodated. Addition times range from 240 to 420 microseconds. Multiplication and division times are 1.9 to 9.6 and 1.3 to 2.4 milliseconds, respectively. Up to forty-nine

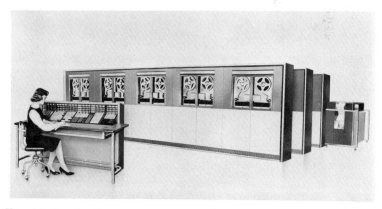

Fig. 10–8. Another recent entry to the high-speed data-processing field is RCA's Model 501.

instructions can be stored. Input-output rates of 33,333 characters per second with magnetic tape and 1000 characters per second with paper tape are available. Prices range from $500,000 to $2,000,000.

A general-purpose computer with a specialized area of application is the RW 300, manufactured by the Thompson-Ramo-Wooldridge Products Co. (also the Philco C-3000 shown in Fig. 10–9). This computer is intended for on-line control of industrial processes. Because of its special type of application, a direct comparison between the RW 300 and the computers previously mentioned cannot be made. Because it must accommodate a variety of processes, each application requires a different set of input-output equipment.

Input information is derived from devices that monitor pertinent process parameters such as liquid flow, weight, temperature, pressure, and similar physical phenomena. Outputs, appearing in digital form, must be translated continuously into electrical or mechanical phenomena capable of controlling parameters similar to the above by means of valves, pumps, heaters, compressors, etc.

The RW 300 uses eighteen-bit binary words. It employs a drum-type memory that is capable of storing more than 8000 words and another drum for fast access (1-millisecond average) to sixteen words. Addition time is 910 milliseconds; multiplication and division require approximately 3 milliseconds each. Typical systems sell for from $100,000 to $200,000.

Another special-purpose process-control computer is being manufactured by Philco for the Leeds and Northrup Company. Intended for use in chemical plants, petroleum refineries, electric power plants, atomic energy processes, steel mills, and metalworking plants, the computer's arithmetic unit is being made available by Philco for real-time control of military systems and related applications (see Fig. 10–9).

Fig. 10–9. Process control using digital techniques is made possible by the RW 300, Transac C-3000 manufactured by Philco (shown here), and others for industrial applications.

The Univac Scientific Model 1103 is available in several different forms. Using thirty-six-bit words in straight binary, one version has up to 12,288 words of fast-access magnetic-core storage. A built-in drum stores more than 16,000 words with 17-millisecond access time. Up to ten Uniservo steel-tape transports may be used with tape-to-machine transfer rates of 2130 words per second. Another model of the 1103 operates on binary-coded-decimal information and is intended primarily for data-processing and business applications.

Remington Rand's newest candidates for the computer field are the double-buffered (read in and out simultaneously) Univac 1105 and the completely tubeless Univac Solid-State Computer (see Fig. 10–10).

Also new is the Univac File Computer System intended for the medium-sized field. Featured are drum-type random-access internal memories with a potential storage capacity (using ten drums) of nearly 2 million characters. Average rates for arithmetic processes are: additions and subtractions, 66,000 per minute; multiplications, 19,400 per minute (per multiplier digit); and divisions, 12,900 per minute (per quotient digit). Magnetic-tape and punch-card peripheral equipment is available.

Fig. 10–10.   The various Univac computers have long enjoyed widespread popularity in both scientific and data-processing applications. The Univac Solid-State Computer shown is one of the more recent entries into the field.

INDEX